Developing
GRIP STRENGTH

Developing GRIP STRENGTH

DAVID GENTLE and DAVID WEBSTER

Springfield Books Limited

Published by Springfield Books Limited, Norman Road, Denby Dale, Huddersfield HD8 8TH England

Photography (unless otherwise credited):
Chris of Glasgow
Design and cover photography: Bryan Ledgard
Typesetting: Paul Hicks Limited
Printed and bound in England by the Bath Press

British Library CIP data
Gentle, David
 Developing Grip Strength.
 1. Weight lifting
 1. Title 2. Webster, David, *1928–*
 796.4'1 GV546.5
ISBN 0 947655 10 7 (cased)
     0 947655 08 5 (paperback)

Contents

DEDICATION
To David Gentle's daughter Karen, who
can twist her father around her little finger.

Introduction

This book is designed to help everyone, from the underdeveloped teenager to the sportsman, athlete and weight-trainer, who wishes rapidly to improve and increase his grip strength and fore-arm power.

*Today's world is tough. Only the fittest survive to reach the top and stay there, in whatever their chosen occupation, business or sporting activity. People respect **strength, power** and **endurance** in all walks of life, and all three of these vital resources can be **developed.***

A strong grip is essential for most sports and recreations, and indeed for many crafts and trades. Cricketers, tennis players, gymnasts etc all require good strength of grip. Painters, plasterers, bricklayers and construction workers are examples of tradesmen who require powerful forearms and a good grip. Even everyday pursuits as simple as opening a jar, or tightening a nut or screw, depend on the strength of the hand and lower arms, while in the specialised sphere of bodybuilding or powerlifting any weakness or lack of development in the forearms can result in failure to win contests or to lift your best weights.

*Here you will find everything practical you need to know for **you** to achieve **self-improvement** in this vital element of becoming a **champion** or top contender in your chosen **sport.***

Within these pages there are progressive and detailed exercises designed to aid all groups wishing quickly to double their power of strength – and there you are shown **how to develop an amazing grip.**

A Look at Basic Training Principles

While this book specialises in grip, wrist and forearm power, the basic principles of bodybuilding and strength training must be followed to obtain the quickest and best results. Any form of self-improvement training must be **regular** and consistent, with a **definite goal** in mind.

Set yourself realistic targets to improve your strength and development. Approach your training with a **positive** attitude.

Train regularly. To gain and develop your strength, the training sessions must be frequent and at regular intervals. It aids progress if you establish a regular training routine, exercising at the same time of day, and on the same training days of the week. Try to train at least three times a week if at all possible. The wrists and forearms are composed of very tough and potentially powerful muscles and are capable of receiving plenty of exercise. Daily exercise of the forearms is quite acceptable.

When exercising, keep warm, avoiding draughts and chills. Maintain a normal and sensible healthy routine. Take any medical problems to your own doctor, no matter how small. Simple illnesses and low-grade infections will seriously hamper all training efforts and delay progress.

You must eat a regular healthy and balanced diet. You need **carbohydrates** (sugars and starches) to provide your body with immediate energy. You need **fats,** which supply longer-term energy reserves. Perhaps most important of all are **proteins,** essential for tissue repair and growth. Dietary **fibre** (bran etc) is vital in a balanced, healthy diet.

You must also obtain daily all the necessary **vitamins** and **minerals** required to maintain good health. The easiest way to ensure this is to take a multivitamin tablet daily with your main meal.

Finally, ensure you drink plenty of pure **water.**

If you are overweight, find out the calorific value of the common foods you normally eat. You must then deliberately cut down and consume less calories. If you are consuming 3,000 Calories or more a day, then cut down to 2,500 or less. By taking 1,000 Calories a day less, you should lose as much as a whole pound a day. Cut out high-calorie foods such as sweets, puddings, pastries and cakes. Substitute instead lean meats, fish, poultry, eggs, vegetables and fruits. Extra exercise over a long period will aid weight reduction, by making you use up more calories, through using extra energy. However, the only **sure** way to lose weight is through diet.

To gain weight, first have a check-up with your doctor to ensure there is no medical reason for your underweight condition. If he gives the OK then:

(a) Try to obtain more rest and relaxation.

(b) Take up bodybuilding, ensuring you exercise the large muscle groups primarily. Exercise the hips and thighs with squats or deep knee bends, the chest with press-ups or bench presses, and the large back muscles known as the "lats" with pull-ups or chins, or by using one of the various "rowing" movements.

(c) Most important of all is simply to **eat more.** To gain weight you have to eat more than your energy requirements. Eat the foods high in calories, such as thick soups, stews, puddings, chocolates, sweets, and creamy foods, especially milk.

Highly recommended are the easily obtainable protein drinks which, when mixed with milk, will soon add extra muscle.

The normalising of your body weight will all help in your quest for building amazing grip strength.

Anatomy of the Hand and Forearm

The human hand is unique in its amazing range of use. Its flexibiity and dexterity are astounding, and its sense of touch is uniquely sensitive. Even the ape family, which resembles man so closely in many other directions, lacks the full development and the ultimate working of the human hand. The range of movement and feeling is remarkable, from refined movements as in music and art, to powerful movements as in sports and manual trades, or the sheer pounding and smashing of the fists in contact sports or fighting.

The bones

The hand consists of twenty-seven bones: eight in the wrist, known as the **carpus** bones; five in the open palm, the **metacarpus** bones, and the fourteen bones of the **phalanges** or fingers and thumb. Over the bones of the hand there are five layers of muscles.

In the forearm there are two bones: the principal one is called the **ulna** and the smaller bone, which assists in the movement of the lower arm, is called the **radius.**

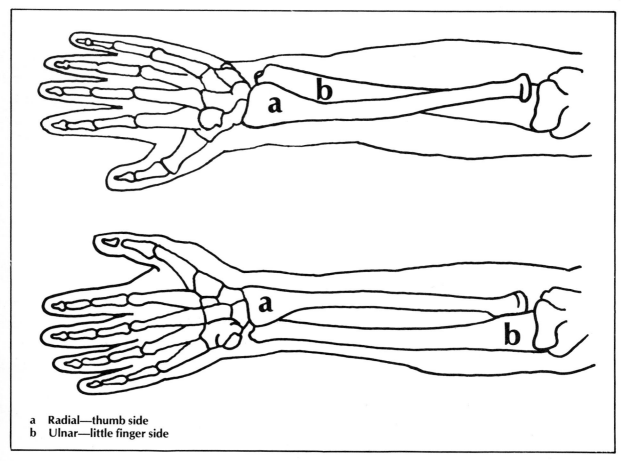

a   Radial—thumb side
b   Ulnar—little finger side

The muscles

Because of the complexity of the fore-arm, wrist and hand, with their great number of muscles, anatomical terminology is here kept to a minimum, the descriptions being largely limited to the location and action of the principal muscle groups involved in the strength and development of these areas.

The prime movers can be divided into the following categories:

Flexors and **extensors** of the elbow joint, involving some muscles attached to the radius and ulna.

Supinators — turning the palm upwards. When fully supinated the radius lies parallel to the ulna.

Pronators — turning the palm of the hand downwards and crossing the radius over the ulna.

Flexors — these flex the wrists and the fingers. Forward bending of the hand is called palmer flexion.

Extensors — these extend the fingers and wrist (in **hyperextension** the back of the hand is brought as close to the forearm as possible — this is often called dorsiflexion).

Adductors — moving the hand to the thumb side of the wrist, sometimes called **radial deviation.**

Circumduction — a circular movement combining all the above movements of the wrist.

The forearm may be considered somewhat unbalanced with the flexor muscles on the front of the arm being capable of more spectacular size than the extensor muscles on the back of the forearm, but the definition of the latter can be very impressive. The majority of forearm muscles act on one or more joints, and are engaged in the flexing and extending of the arm or the bending and twisting of the elbow. Also involved is the flexion of the wrist joint, that is, the moving of the palm towards the forearm. Finally you have the sideways movement of adduction, bending the wrist on the heel side of the hand, and abduction, the reverse, which involves bending the thumb side of the hand inwards to the forearm.

You will see that there is considerable flexibility and complexity in the make-up of the muscles of the forearm, wrist and hand, and it should be apparent that with so many muscles there is the potential to develop a grip and forearm capable of **great power.**

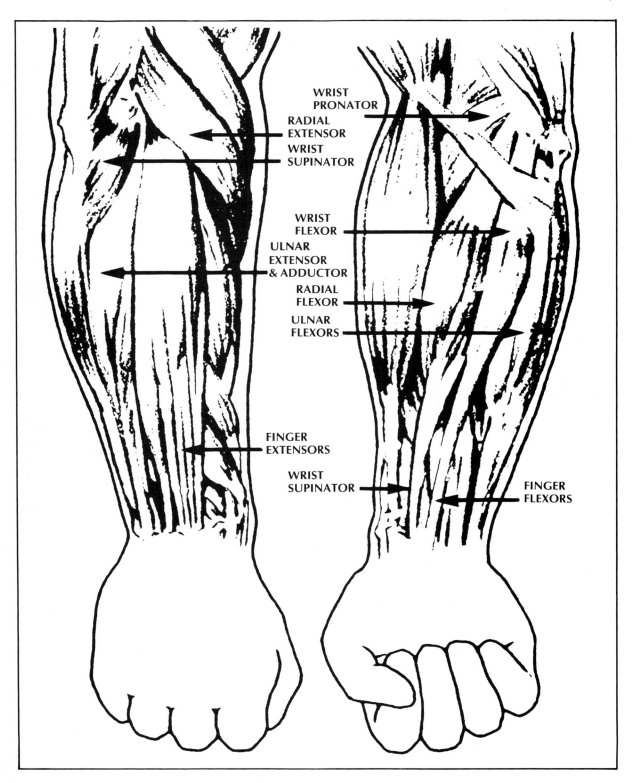

WRIST
PRONATOR

RADIAL
EXTENSOR

WRIST
SUPINATOR

WRIST
FLEXOR

ULNAR
EXTENSOR
& ADDUCTOR

RADIAL
FLEXOR

ULNAR
FLEXORS

FINGER
EXTENSORS

WRIST
SUPINATOR

FINGER
FLEXORS

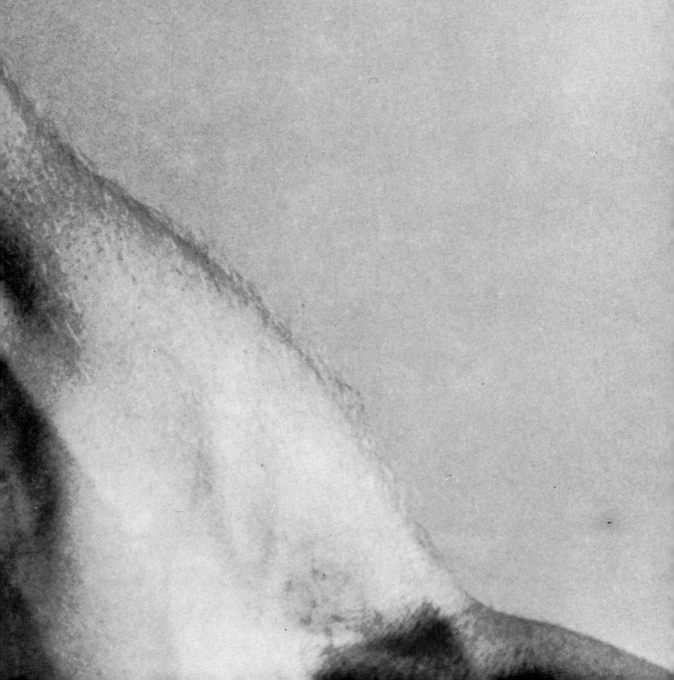

GRIP STRENGTH EXERCISES

Forearm Exercises Without Apparatus

Those who are seeking an excuse for not training will be disappointed to find that grip and forearm training costs very little in terms of either special apparatus or of time.

Many everyday objects can be converted into training gear, and forearm and grip training can be slotted into any small period of time. Other equipment used, such as hand grips and rubber gripping packs, is very inexpensive, and the special weight-training exercises are easily practised between the main exercises at home or at the gym.

The following exercises have been tried and tested over many years, and have proved to be excellent strength and muscle developers. They require no apparatus or expensive equipment and can be practised almost anywhere or at any time. Regular and faithful practice of several of the following exercises will soon show results.

Exercise one
Simply grasp your hands together and alternately grip with all your power first the left hand and then the right. Continue, using plenty of energy and power, until the gripping muscles of the hands and forearms are tired.

Exercise two
Clench your right fist and twist it in a clockwise direction, to the right. Hold your right fist with the left hand and now attempt to twist your fist in an anti-clockwise direction, to the left, all the time resisting strongly with the left hand. Repeat several times, then change the position of your hands and give the left fist the corresponding exercise.

Exercise three
Similar to the above except that you commence with the right fist twisted anti-clockwise, to the left. You then resist the clockwise movement with the left hand. Reverse your hands, and repeat.

Exercise four
Start with the right fist clenched, palm facing downwards, and wrist bent fully

downwards. Place the left hand on top of the right wrist and attempt to raise the right fist, at the same time resisting strongly with the left hand. Perform about twelve to fifteen movements, fully bending and extending the right wrist, while resisting with the left hand. As you grow stronger, use more and more firm resistance. Change the position of the hands, and repeat.

Exercise five

This time commence with wrist tensed, palm facing upwards. Resist as in the previous exercise, changing hands to give both wrists and forearms equal work.

Exercise six

The so-called "gooseneck" contraction of the forearm is a superb muscle control exercise which gives a fine workout to the lower arm flexors and rotators. The fist is tightly clenched and the wrist bent as much as possible before being turned slowly to a position where the hand is similar to the head of a goose, the forearm its neck and the upper arm the body of the bird. In this position all the muscles can be very strongly tensed.

Repeat ten times with each arm, striving each time for a full contraction. Later both arms can be exercised at the same time.

Below: **Hand grasping**

Overleaf: **'Gooseneck' contraction of forearm**

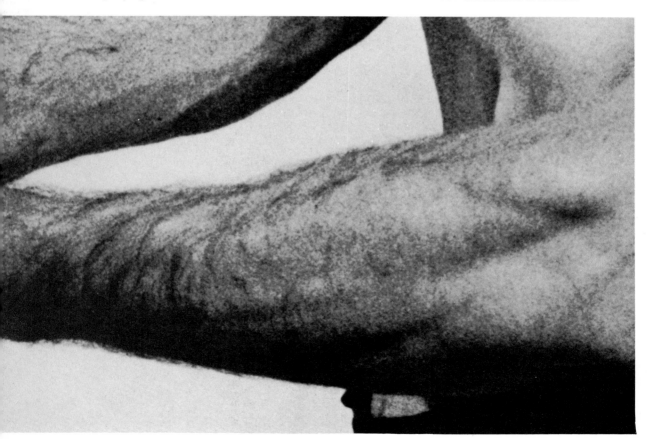

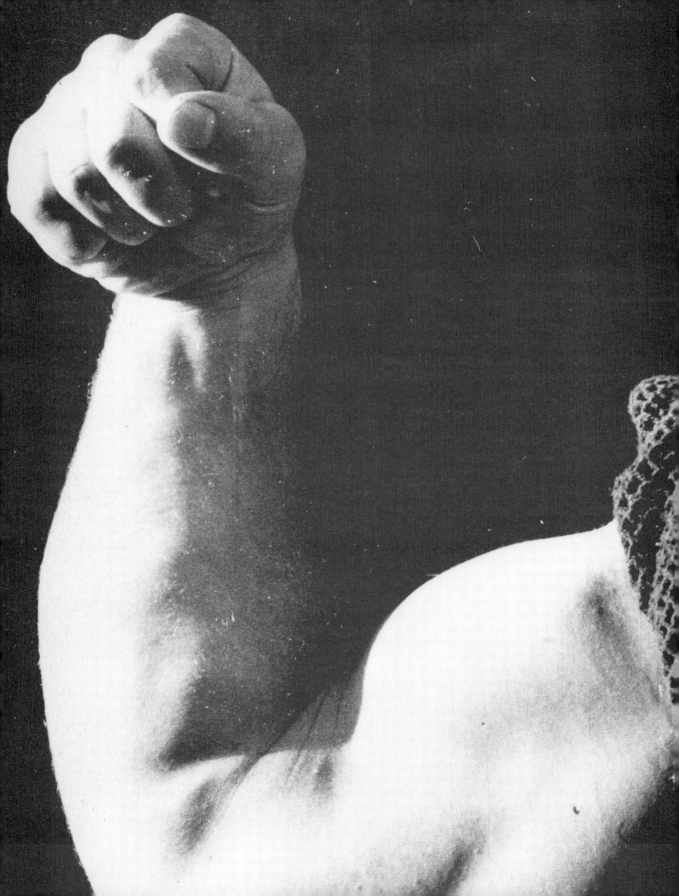

Finger Tougheners and Strengtheners

Like the forearms, the fingers will show a rapid improvement in strength with progressive training. Do not be put off by the simplicity of the movements.

Regular practice will bring results.

Exercise one

With the palm face up, exercise one single finger at a time by curling the finger into the palm, at the same time resisting the movement with the opposite hand. Give equal exercise to all the fingers, using about a dozen or so movements. Exercise fully the fingers on both hands.

Exercise two

Place the hand face down on a table top, and on top of the fingers place a fairly heavy book. Attempt to raise the book by extending one or two fingers at a time. You can make this exercise progressive by gradually using heavier or more books as resistance.

Exercise three

As above, but this time commence with the palm upwards, thus exercising the flexor muscles.

Exercise four

Press the hands together with fingers outspread as wide as they will go. Strongly press the fingers of both hands together for about ten seconds, pressing as hard as you can. Rest and repeat.

Exercise five

Tightly grip the fist and — while tensing powerfully — bend and twist the wrist in all directions. Rest and repeat several more times.

All of the foregoing exercises take up just a few minutes, and can be practised any time you wish, either during the day, or in the evening.

Below: **Wrist turning**

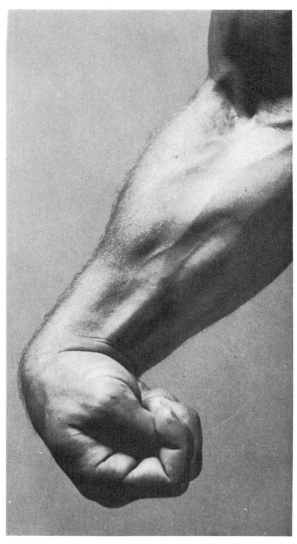

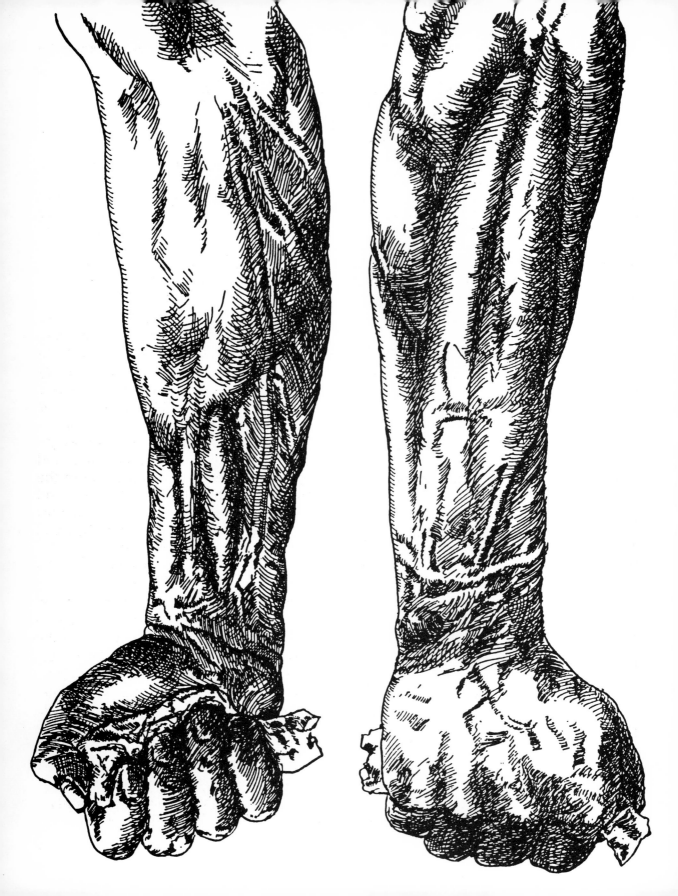

Grip Exercises Without Special Apparatus

The following exercises for hands, wrists and forearms can all be practised on a regular and progressive basis, using readily obtainable everyday objects. No special apparatus or expense is required to rapidly improve both strength and development of grip and lower arms. In many instances other muscles are called into play in the following exercises, giving you a bonus of extra strength with your training.

Most of the exercises can be carried out during spare moments of the day, so there is no excuse for saying that you have not got the time to train.

Pick out two or three exercises which appeal to you, gradually increasing your efforts with continued practice. You can change exercises from time to time to give variety and thereby help to maintain your interest.

Squeezing a rubber ball

The regular practice of squeezing a small rubber ball is excellent exercise for the hands, wrists and forearms. The ball can be carried in your pocket, and the exercise can be practised at any time you wish or find convenient.

Attempt to squeeze and really crush the ball, tighter and tighter; also practise rolling it around and between individual fingers. Continued gripping and relaxing of the ball will aid endurance as well as power.

Rolling up sheets of newspaper

Spread out a newspaper full-size on the table, then with one hand, and starting from one corner, gradually roll the paper up into a tight ball. Finally, squash up the finished roll of paper as tight as you possibly can. Repeat with the other hand to give both hands equal exercise.

Tearing telephone directories or thick books in half

An extension of the previous idea is to try to tear in half old books, catalogues, or the more commonly recognised feat, telephone directories. Commence with a medium-sized telephone book, preferably one which is out of date! There are two ways to do this feat. One method is as follows. Start with the pages facing away from you, curl your fists around the edges of the pages with thumbs on top and fingers underneath, soften the end of the book by bending the directory up and down, slightly splaying the pages almost fan-like, and then attempt to tear the book in half starting with a few pages, until you are tearing the whole thickness of the book in two halves. The other method is to start off with the bound, or resin-glued spine. Using maximum strength, try to break the spine in half; this will have the effect of breaking all the bound pages, which you will then be able to tear, finishing up with tearing the whole telephone directory in two. For progression, attempt thicker books or even try to tear two at a time.

Opposite: **Gripping paper (or rubber balls). Grip with the fingers; do not overlap with the thumb.**

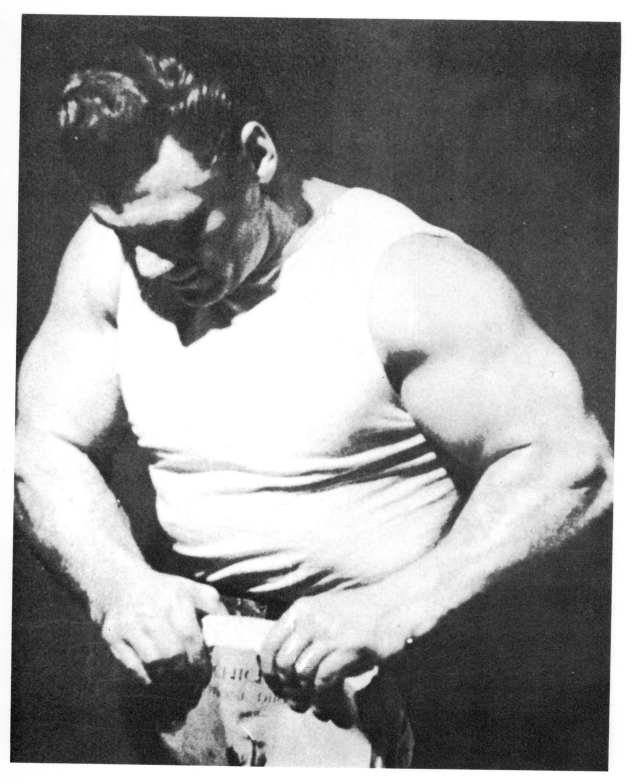

Breaking matches between the fingers

This is more of a stunt than an exercise, but one that demonstrates finger power. Place a full-length matchstick between the first and third fingers of either hands just below the fingernails. The second finger is positioned over the match. With fingers straight, you have to try to break the match by pressing down with the second finger. Vary the exercise by placing the match between different fingers. The next progression is to try breaking two matches at a time.

Opposite: **The mighty John Grimek tears a massive Chicago telephone directory in half**

Below: **Breaking matches with finger tips**

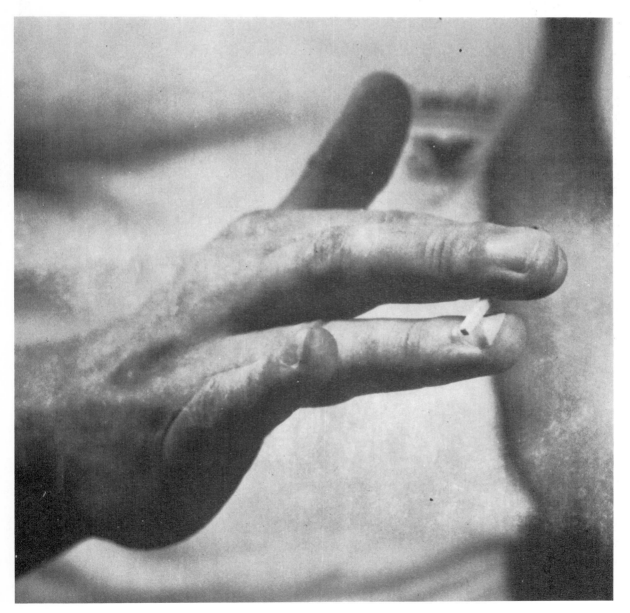

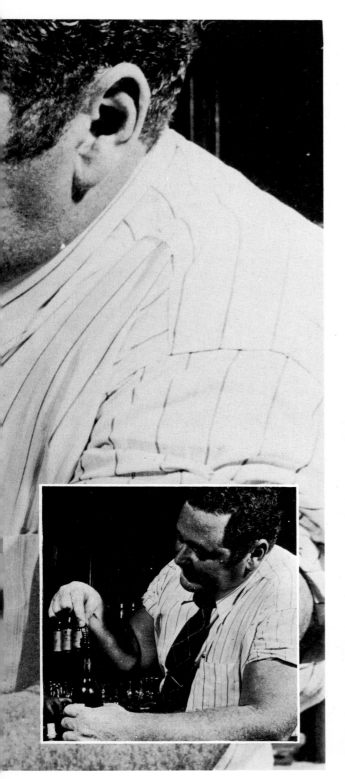

Squashing bottle tops

Some beer or mineral bottles have tops made of corrugated metal, with cork centres. A good finger exercise is to place the cap between finger and thumb, or indeed any two digits, and attempt to fold the bottle top into two. If one is easy, then try several between different fingers.

More readily available with modern packaging are the metal drink cans which can be used for the next exercise.

Big Mac Batchelor, a 300 lb Californian barman, was undefeated in over twenty years in these bar-room tests of grip strength

Left and inset: **Bending beer caps between thumb and finger to see who was first to fill the bottle with bent caps**

Below: **The triple crusher—bending three beer caps at one time**

Squashing beer cans

Most carbonated drinks are now marketed in metal cans. These vary slightly in strength and size, but are excellent objects upon which to practise your grip strength. As well as crushing them with hand power, you can also try squashing them with karate-type blows, and even to try to tear them in half. With a growing strength you could progress to bending and tearing ever-increasing thicknesses of metal plate. Bill Pearl – Mr Universe several times over – demonstrates his power regularly at shows, by tearing metal car-licence plates in half.

Left: **Mac 'walks' his fingers up a bottle**

Below: **A leverage pinch grip**

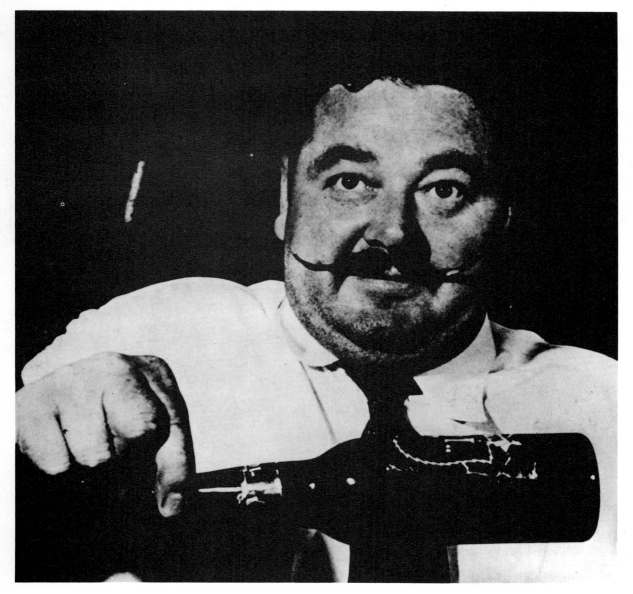

Tearing a pack of cards

This stunt is probably not practical for regular training because of the sheer expense of buying playing cards. However, it is a recognised feat of strength and well worth occasional practice, especially if you make the effort to obtain some second-hand cards. This is harder than directory tearing, because of the lesser leverage possible on the smaller area of a pack of cards, so a really strong grip is needed. Grasp the cards tightly in one hand, then, when you are satisfied with your hold, grip equally strongly with the other hand, attempting to bend the cards in half to break up some of their strong fibres. You then twist the hands in opposite directions as

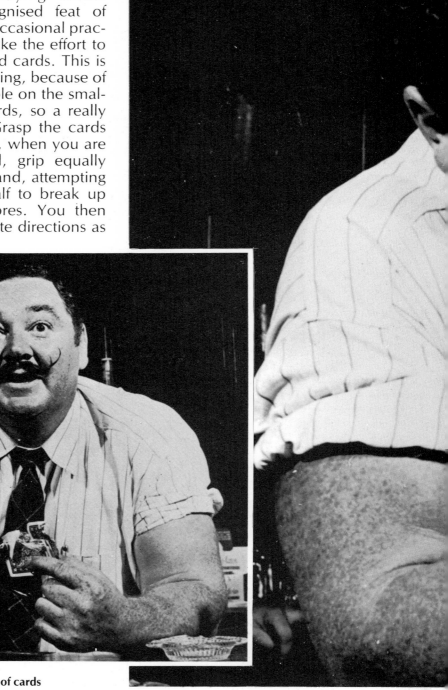

Showing how easily he tears a pack of cards

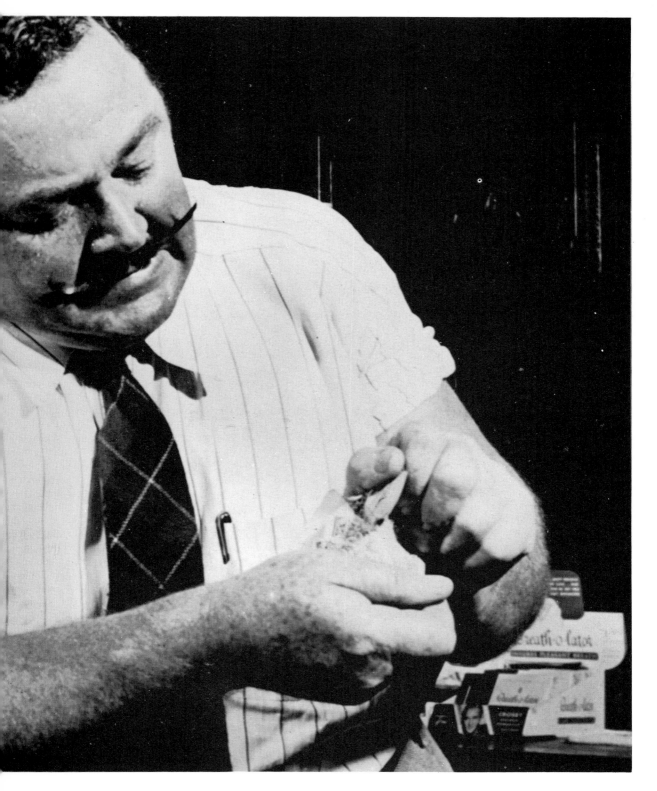

hard as you can, all of the time gripping the cards very tightly. With continued effort, you will be rewarded by the cards tearing in half. Really strong men can tear several packs in half at the same time. One of the best was the early American strength athlete Al Treloar who would end his strong-man show (circa 1910-11) by tearing four packs of cards in half, all at the same time. He later discontinued this, however, as it took so long to do, and so much effort, that it was not considered practical to include in a strong-man demonstration.

Below: **Bill Pearl tearing a licence plate**

Self-resistance exercises

An interesting variety of resistance exercises can be done using a towel or a short length of rope or chain etc. The basic principle is that the working arm does one of the wrist or forearm movements, turning, twisting, curling etc, while the other arm provides just enough resistance to allow the exercise to be done correctly. This self-resistance can be finely judged, for who knows better than you how much effort is required?

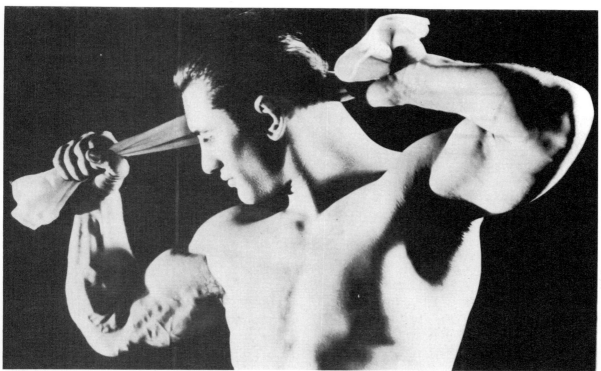

Above: **Clevio Massimo—self-resistance exercise with towel**

Below: **Although his arms were massively developed and very strong, Massimo was a professional musician with a delicate touch**

Floor dips on finger tips

A good exercise to strengthen fingers is to practise the standard floor dip or press-up exercise using outspread fingers, putting your weight on to your finger tips instead of the palms. You can begin the press-ups on all fingers, and then gradually attempt to support your weight on three or even two fingers of each hand. Some people, usually practitioners of handbalancing, have been able to achieve this feat using just one finger of each hand. Foremost in this type of finger balance was an early American balancer by the name of Bob Jones from Philadelphia. His most sensational feat was being able to balance on his **thumbs,** on top of two Indian clubs, in the handstand position. Bob Jones was featured many times in the muscle magazines of the day. The famous Ripley's *Believe It or Not* publications featured Jones many times doing his herculean finger balances.

While on the subject of finger balancing, I am well aware that several circus performers claim to be able to balance on a bottle-like object "with one finger" (supposedly the index finger). I am also aware that this stunt is carried out with the aid of a hidden tube (often in a glove) which in fact strengthens and supports the single digit. Standing on the **thumb** is an entirely different leverage principle, and Bob Jones did **not** use any such secret aids.

While strength feats such as bending iron bars, breaking horseshoes, and tearing books and cards, involve the hands, wrists and forearms, they also

Right: **Floor dips (press-ups) on finger tips**

Far right: **Robert L Jones, thumb balancing athlete supreme**

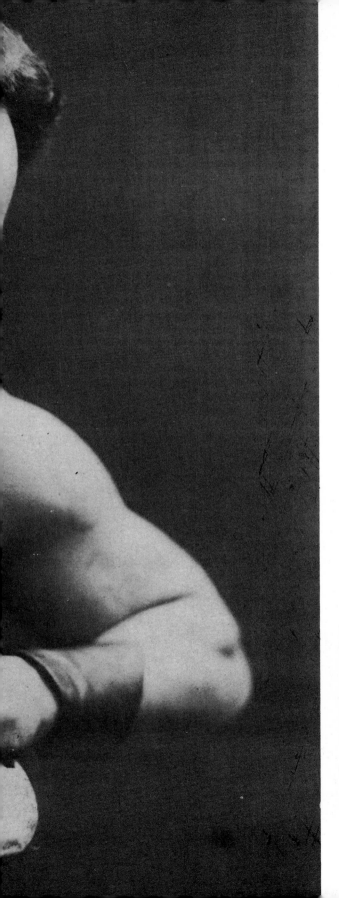

call heavily into play various other groups of muscles of the upper arms, chest, shoulders, back and abdomen; and indeed they need all-round bodily strength and vigorous energy expenditure. Thus training for strength feats of grip and forearm is also good all-round exercise.

Whether you pull or push, gripping these objects is excellent isometric exercise.

Left: **Pierre Gasnier, of the Barnum & Bailey circus, breaking a horseshoe**

Below: **Another form of self-resistance exercise**

Forearm exercises with weights

The following exercises are recognised as the best one can perform with weights to develop great strength and mobility of the forearms and wrists.

Wrist roller exercise

Tie a barbell plate to a length of cord. Attach a short rod to the other end of the cord. The exercise is to wind the weight up to the rod by twisting the wrists. The cord should be at least a metre long.

Opposite: **Wrist roller exercise**
Below left: **Roller in rectangular fix position**
Below right: **Wrist roller palms upwards**

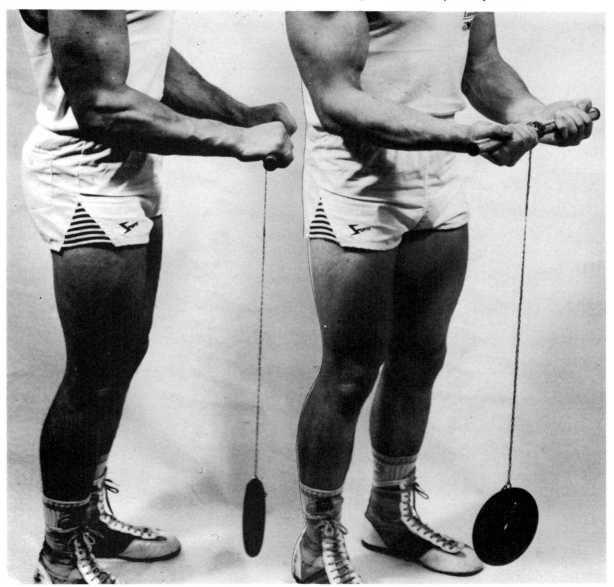

The seated barbell wrist curl with palms facing downwards

Seated at the end of a bench, grasp a barbell with both hands, using a palms-down grip with your hands about twelve inches apart. Lean forwards and place your forearms on the top of your knees with the barbell hanging downwards. Lower the barbell to the lowest possible position your wrists will allow. Then with pure wrist and forearm strength lift the barbell as high as your wrists will go. Ensure the movement is by wrist power alone. Lower and repeat about twelve to fifteen times. It is normal to use more repetitions for forearms than for most other weight-training exercises, as the forearms are tough and need plenty of reps to help produce the greatest growth and power. Casey Viator, a famous American physique star noted for his association with the unique Nautilus physical-training machines, uses well over 200 lb (90 kg) for this exercise. But a word of warning: start off by using very light weights in all exercises until you know your strength. And always commence with a light weight for the first set of exercises to help prevent injury or muscle strain.

Opposite: **The wrist roller. Note the fine wrist action**

Below: **Seated wrist curl with palms upwards**

The seated barbell wrist curl with palms facing upwards

Seated at the end of your bench as in the previous exercise, grasp a barbell as before with the hands about a foot apart, but this time have the palms facing upwards. With the bar just hanging over the knees, as in the first exercise, curl the barbell to the maximum extent, using only the power of your wrists and forearms. Ensure you keep the forearms still on your thighs, using no momentum or swing to lift the barbell. Try twelve to fifteen repetitions for one set. As you get stronger and your wrists are capable of more exercise, you can increase the weight of the barbell, making sure to do so gradually; and then you may also increase the number of sets. An advanced trainer would do up to six sets when concentrating on forearms. In a normal routine, three sets of twelve repetitions (3 x 12) would suffice for satisfactory exercise.

Seated dumb-bell wrist curls

This exercise is similar to the previous exercises with barbells, but because of the use of dumb-bells it allows even greater range of movement for the wrists and forearms. It can be done with one or two dumb-bells, but perhaps more concentrated exercise can be achieved if you use only one dumb-bell at a time, changing hands to give both wrists and forearms equal work.

Load up a small dumb-bell, and rest your forearms on your thigh, with the wrist and dumb-bell overhanging, as in the barbell movements. First of all do the wrist curls with palms facing downwards, then try several sets using the dumb-bells with the palms facing upwards, thus exercising all the forearm muscles, both extensors and flexors.

Opposite: **Household objects can be used for grip strengthening exercises; here an ordinary flat iron is used for single hand curls**

Below: **Dumb-bell wrist curls with palms upwards**

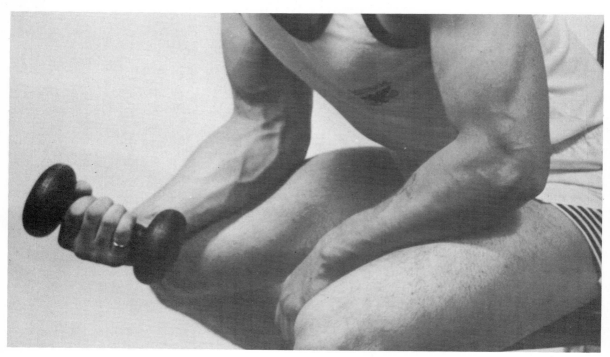

Standing wrist curls with barbell held behind the back

Step in front of a fairly light barbell, and lift it up so that it is held behind your back at hip height. Place the hands about a foot apart, and with palms facing away from your back, using wrist movement alone, curl the barbell to the maximum extent of your wrist range, upwards towards your shoulders. Lower and repeat about twelve times, concentrating on good wrist movements and involving the forearms. Keep the arms straight and use only wrist power to lift the barbell. Rest and repeat for more sets as and when your strength allows. A light barbell is quite enough to start with until you get used to the move, after which you can progress, as in all exercises, by adding more weight to the bar for extra resistance.

Standing wrist curls with bar held in front of the body, palms facing downwards

The title of this exercise explains itself. Simply lift a barbell to hip height in front of your body, with palms facing downwards. Without any other movement, but by pure wrist strength, raise the barbell to its highest position, hold for a second, then lower. Perform the usual number of repetitions (normally between 12 to 20), rest and then repeat for another set as required.

Wrist curls with dumb-bells held at the sides

With dumb-bells held at your sides in both hands, thumb facing to the front, using wrist and forearm power alone, curl the dumb-bells outwards and then

**Wrist curls with barbell held behind back
(palms backwards and forwards)**

Wrist curls on preacher bench

Wrist extensions on preacher bench

inwards, to the full extent of your wrists' flexibility. Continue until the forearms are really pumped with muscular exertion. Rest and repeat for several sets, or until you are tired.

Seated wrist turns with dumb-bells

For even greater concentration, the previous exercise can be practised while seated on your exercise bench. Remember to try to move the wrists in each direction.

Preacher bench wrist curls

A further variation on wrist curls both with barbells and dumb-bells can be found if you do the exercises over an exercise bench known as a "preacher bench". If you are not familiar with this term, the name will give you a clue as to what it means; the bench is similar to the "old time" preacher's book rest, i.e. a short inclined board over which you can lay your arms. This exercise really isolates the arms preventing any superfluous movements or cheating. Try exercising your forearms with this aid, using barbells and dumb-bells in all the exercises described above.

Below: **Single arm curl using a plastic dumb-bell of a type becoming increasingly popular with girls and women**

Wrist curls with barbell or dumb-bells overhanging bench

Again the title describes the exercises. You need a fairly high bench, one that enables you to lie prone (i.e. face down to the floor) over the bench with the barbell or dumb-bell hanging down over the end. The exercise is to curl the bar with the wrist strength alone. Always remember to use light weights to warm up, adding extra weight in later sets for strength and power.

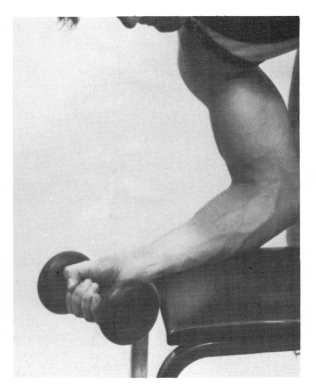

Above: **Wrist curls over edge of bench**

Below: **Wrist extensions over edge of bench**

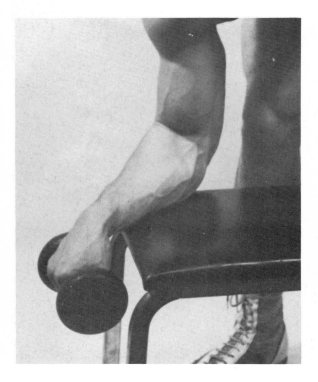

Leverage bar exercises

A very useful form of forearm exercise is the type using lever bars. This kind of exercise was derived from commonly practised strength stunts such as attempting to lift brushes or long-handled tools by the end of their handles, or lifting a chair by one leg. It is a good test of wrist power to lift a standard kitchen chair by the extreme end of one chair leg. To perform this feat you must:

(a) squat down and grasp the bottom of the chair leg with a strong grip;

(b) tip the chair slightly towards you into the balance position;

(c) lift the chair up and out with your arm held straight out in front, at shoulder height. For tougher work, graduate to heavier chairs.

Bill Hunt, a grip specialist, adds extra weights to the seat of his challenge chair, and is unbeaten at this particular event.

The idea of using common objects as an exercise medium has been fully explored by several successful mail order muscle-building courses.

Joe Price, a former blacksmith turned weight-lifter, marketed a muscle-building course using many ingenious exercises involving a sledgehammer.

Old-timer Edward Aston, once Britain's strongest man (he could lift over 300 lb overhead with **one hand)** brought

Below: **Joe Price, champion blacksmith and lifter**

Above: **A brush is used as a leverage bar. The further the hand from the brush head, the more testing the exercise**

Right: **W J (Bill) Hunt, ex-Olympic champion and champion of grip strength stunts**

out a lever bell, as also did the famous strong man and writer George F. Jowett. Even Muscledom's best businessman and multi-magazine owner Joe Weider gave space and much attention to the idea in his magazines in the 1950s, with Canadian star Leo Roberts illustrating the exercises. There are some interesting pictures and information about the recent world champion of sledgehammer leverage lifting in that fascinating book *The Mighty Atom* by Joe Greenstein.

Lever bar

To make yourself a lever bar, take a dumb-bell rod and fasten at one end only a light 2 or 3 kilogram disc. Secure the disc tightly with a collar, and grasp the bar at the opposite unweighted end.

Hold the bar tightly and, with wrist and forearm power, move the loaded end around in circles, up and down, and from side to side. Get as much full-range movement as possible without moving the elbows or upper arms. You can work with each arm individually, or with a longer, heavier bar use both hands together.

Regular practice with this lever bar, which can be made progressively tougher by using more weight, will greatly improve your forearms and wrists.

The severity of the exercise can also be varied by the distance the bar is held from the weight. The greater the distance the harder the exercise.

A similar principle, but involving the fingers more specifically, lies behind the various strength challenges using objects

Below: **Lifting a chair by one leg. (It is easiest if you start with a back leg)**

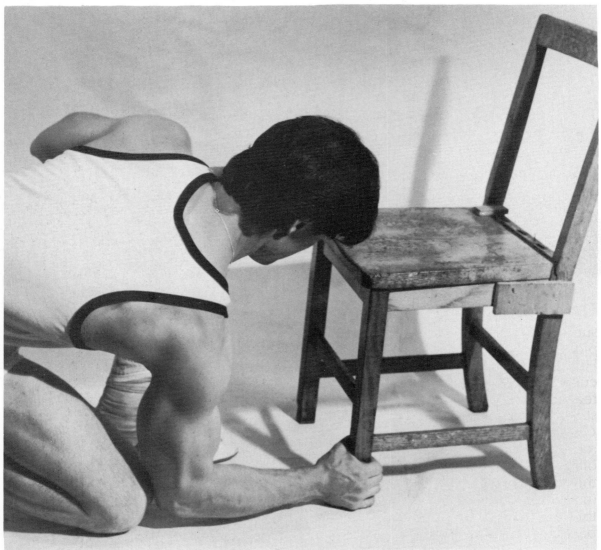

such as billiard or pool cues. The champion at this has for many years been Bill Hunt from Lancashire. A grand physical culturist for all his long life, Bill has been featured in many magazines and strength books, and regularly in the *Guinness Book of Records* with his record-breaking stunt of levering six billiard cues by their tips simultaneously through ninety degrees to the horizontal (using just fingers without the aid of the thumb support). Bill, a herculean hand-balancer, has always specialised in grip strength, and crushes bottle tops be-

tween his fingers.

Now over 70 years old, Bill is training a protege, Mike Bolton, with some success, as young Mike already holds records in this type of work.

Above: **Lever bar exercises**

Overleaf: **Fantastic finger strength of cue lifting record holder J Mills**

Inset overleaf: **At age 57, Bert Briggs of Darwen levered a 22 oz cue for 117 reps—an extraordinary feat of finger strength**

Heavy weight training exercises

The previous exercises were isolated and specialised exercises employing pure wrist and forearm mobility. All of them can be made harder by gradually adding extra weight, until you are using some respectable poundages.

We now continue to some basic exercises which in themselves use perhaps the greatest of all weights possible, i.e. the exercise known as **dead lifts**.

Two-handed dead lift

This exercise is termed the "dead lift" because you are lifting a "dead weight", i.e. a weight from the still position without any momentum or swing, unlike the snatch or clean and jerk where velocity is all-important. The dead lift did **not** get its name, as some people think, because you often feel half-dead from practising it!

Load up a reasonably weighted barbell, remembering the old and wise safety practice of **ensuring that you are thoroughly warmed up** before you try to lift heavy weights. With your hands about shoulder width apart, palms facing the floor, and your **back straight** at all times, bend over the bar and, using mainly leg strength, lift the barbell until you are in an upright position with the bar held in front at hip height. This exercise is very basic, and yet it is the greatest builder of power for the back and grip ever known. You must be careful to ensure you have the proper position when lifting, maintaining a straight spine. Do **not** curl forwards or arch the back, but use the strength of your hips and legs. You will soon discover that, when you are trying to lift maximum weights, there is a tendency

for the bar to roll out of your grasp, which is why in record lifting the **hands are placed in reversed positions,** i.e. one hand faces one way, and the other hand faces the other way, thus preventing the bar from rolling out of the fingers.

For a **back** exercise, some top power-

Opposite: **The dead lift is a good single exercise. Ray Nobile (Scotland), European power champion 1980 (100 kg class)**

Below: **Major St John Turner created four veteran records when over 80 years old**

lifters use wrist straps, thereby aiding their gripping power. Paul Anderson, thought by many to have been the strongest man ever, often lifted over a thousand pounds (1,000 lb) in the dead lift, with the aid of straps. Naturally, for improving your grip strength you do not use straps, but instead try to lift as much as possible in the normal unaided grip.

A variation of dead lifting is to try **straddle lifting.** This variation is done by stepping over the bar with one leg, or in other words straddling the bar. You then lift the bar to the upright position, standing erect with the bar held between the legs. Lots of weight can be used in this exercise, which is a great leg and back developer, as well as excellent exercise for the grip.

Single-handed dead lift

From two-handed dead lifts, you can progress to single-handed dead lifts. You may be amazed to find that you can lift almost as much with one hand as you can with two. This exercise can be practised either with the bar in front of the body, or as in the straddle lift, with the bar between the legs. In fact most people find the second method easier, as it allows for better balance.

Finally, you can try lifting the weights in dead-lift style with any number of fingers, usually trying to see how much you can lift with two fingers of each hand, or perhaps just one finger of each hand. This is certainly a great way to strengthen your fingers and your total hand strength. Using thick-handled weights or lifting by the outside sleeve of competition barbells is particularly tough on the grip.

Of course, anyone who embarks on a weight-training course will get plenty of exercise for the forearms in many of the

Single handed dead lift

other standard exercises, especially the varieties of curls for the biceps, but for technical reasons the following form of curl is best for the forearms.

The reverse curl

The reverse curl or backhanded curl is so named because the barbell is grasped with the back of the hand uppermost. The normal weight lifted in this method, a far superior forearm developer, is approximately 85% of that which can be used in the regular palms-upward curl.

Using a medium-loaded barbell, with hands about shoulder width apart, and with knuckles uppermost, lift the bar to

Rectangular fix

Inset: **Rectangular fix with a light 'beauty bar' for women**

Rectangular fix and reverse curl with spring device

Rectangular fix and reverse curl with ordinary strands

waist height; keep the elbows close to the sides and, using forearm power, curl the bar to the shoulders. Hold for a few seconds, then lower in a controlled fashion. About three or four sets of twelve repetitions should give anyone a good workout.

Rarely practised now, this exercise used to be part of the strength test known as the **rectangular fix,** where the weight was reverse curled to the horizontal or half-way position, and then held for several seconds before being lowered. Arthur Dandurand, who is mentioned in other chapters, is credited

Opposite: **John Citrone using an expander. Note how firmly he holds the handle with his left foot**

with reverse curling 177.5 lb when he himself weighed only 182 lb, a remarkable achievement.

An alternative means of training

The wrist curl, slow curl, reverse curl, rectangular fix and other such movements can all be done as strand-pulling exercises as opposed to weight-training ones. Strand-pulling is the correct name for "chest expanders", for the efficiency of the apparatus is not limited to improving the chest. By placing a handle under one foot **and firmly keeping the toes on the ground so that the handle does not slip,** a good range of wrist, forearm and arm exercises can be performed.

Pinch gripping weights

A superb exercise to develop grip and flexor strength of the hands and forearm is the practice of **pinch gripping.** This means lifting weights by pinching the edge of the discs with the fingers. Recognised lifts are only those which use plates with smooth sides or ends, not the type with a sunken ridge which would naturally make the feat easier. While magnesium carbonate chalk or floor dust are accepted to counteract slippery fingers or discs, no other aids are allowed. The weights are to be lifted by pure pincer-like thumb and finger gripping power.

Although some consider a successful lift to be one where the discs simply clear the floor, it is more customary to stand properly erect with the weights before lowering them. This would count as one repetition. In training you should do eight to twelve reps in a set. The way to strength in pinch gripping weights, as in all other strength methods, is via steady progression against increasing resistance. Start with small discs and work your way up.

An interesting account of pinch-lifting competitions was given by Ivan Dunbar in the April 1982 issue of *Health and Strength* magazine. The test entailed pinch gripping the heaviest weights possible, and then trying to carry them the length of the gym. The discs in this case were loaded on a swingbell rod, and Ivan won the competition with a worthy 72½ lb. Ivan says he must have developed the strength by having to pick up everyone else's weights and return them to the racks at the end of a training session. I know the feeling!

On 10 July 1934 Hermann Goerner pinch lifted 111 lb in this way, using smooth discs loaded on a chair leg. He was closely matched by the French athlete Louis Uni (stage name Apollon), who until recently had the largest recorded forearms of all time. This may now have been beaten by Cleve Dean of Atlanta, Georgia, who was a contestant in one of the televised "world's strongest man" contests.

Cleve Dean was 6 feet 7 inches tall, weighed 450 lb and had biceps of 23 inches and a forearm of 18 inches. Louis Uni was not as tall or heavy as this, making his earlier famous feats of strength even more praiseworthy.

Without using a bar on which to assemble the discs, but using instead larger discs, or even harder still, just several discs pinched tight together, many fine records have been achieved. Historian of strength feats David Willoughby lists many such records in his fine book *The Super Athletes* (Barnes 1970) including one feat of Apollon (mentioned above) who, using his **four fingers** and the palms of his hand in a bent position, lifted a 90-lb barbell plate which he then "muscled out" i.e. held with straight arms at shoulder height in front of him. This was performed in about 1891/2.

In the June 1945 issue of *Strength and Health*, Robert L. Jones (mentioned elsewhere for his own handbalancing feats) describes the amazing feats of Al Berger from Philadelphia. Al specialised in being able to "chin" himself by pinch-gripping 3-inch-thick rafters, a stunt at which he remained supreme. He also practised lots of pinch lifting, using

Keith Brown demonstrates disc lifting for pinch grip strength

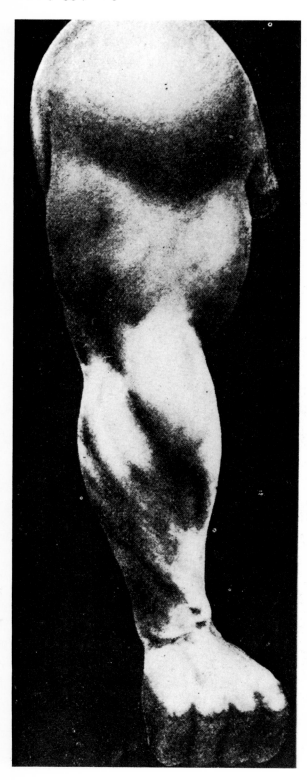

Left: **The impressive arm of Louis Uni, whose forearms were over 16 inches round**

Opposite: **The fabulous former World and Olympic heavyweight lifter John Davis, who won eight World and Olympic championships between 1938 and 1956. Here Davis is pinch-gripping 2 x 35 lb smooth-sided barbell plates**

barbell plates. Al could pinch grip the **flat** sides of two 30-lb barbell plates, lifting the discs to shoulder height in the weight-lifting movement known as the "clean". The same article mentions Al's ability to pinch grip a 75-lb plate with an extra 33-lb weight attached. (His own bodyweight at that time was about 195 lb.) For yet another demonstration of Berger's forearm power, note also his ability to reverse curl a barbell weighing 150 lb.

J.C. Tolson, the British professional strongman, who called himself "The Mighty Apollon" and who ran a successful "train by mail" course, could pinch grip and lift a lead block weighing 65 lb (29.5 kg) to which he had soldered an old penny. The penny was attached to the top of the weight, and Tolson lifted the block by pinching the penny between his forefinger and thumb.

Just a couple more examples of pinch-lifting . . .

Mac Batchelor once pinch-lifted a smooth-sided steel plate weighing 100 lb (45.4 kg)

Bruce White, an Australian wheat farmer, after specialised training on pinch-lifting, raised 115 lb using his thumb and two fingers, the weight consisting of several smooth plates held together on a short bar. White, who is only just under 5 feet 8 inches tall and weighs around 150 lb, held a lightweight Australian record with a 611½ lb dead-lift.

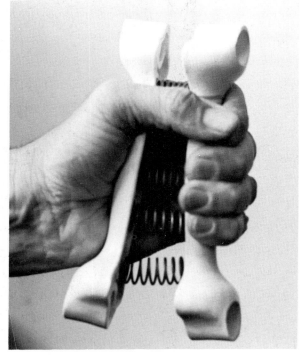

Above: **This special expander handle is designed to improve grip and forearm strength**

Above: **Another spring grip device**

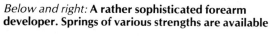

Below and right: **A rather sophisticated forearm developer. Springs of various strengths are available**

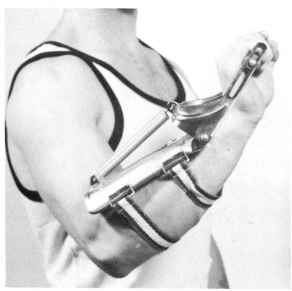

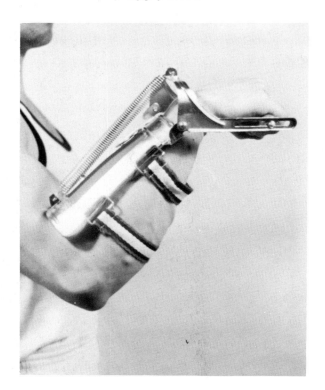

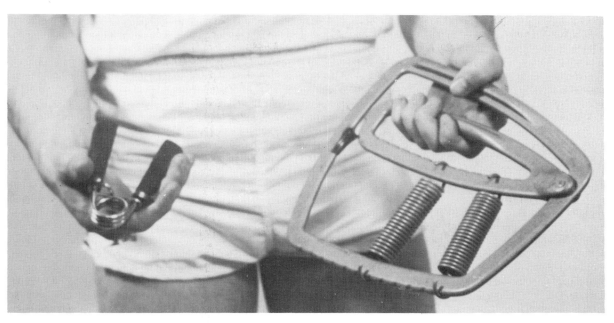

Above: **Two types of gripping device. The one in the left hand gives progressive resistance by adjusting spring position**

Below: **This spring apparatus is called a rower and can be used for forearm and grip exercises**

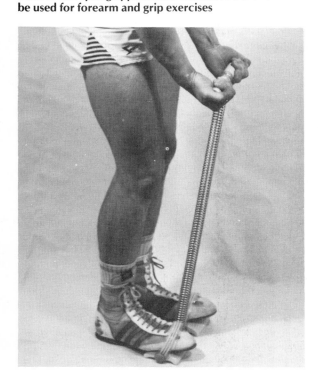

Below: **Disc flipping. Keep the arms still and flip the disc from hand to hand moving only palms and fingers.**

Above: **Wrist rotations. Grip the end of a globe dumb-bell and rotate the hand clockwise and anti-clockwise, ensuring that left and right hands do equal work.**

65

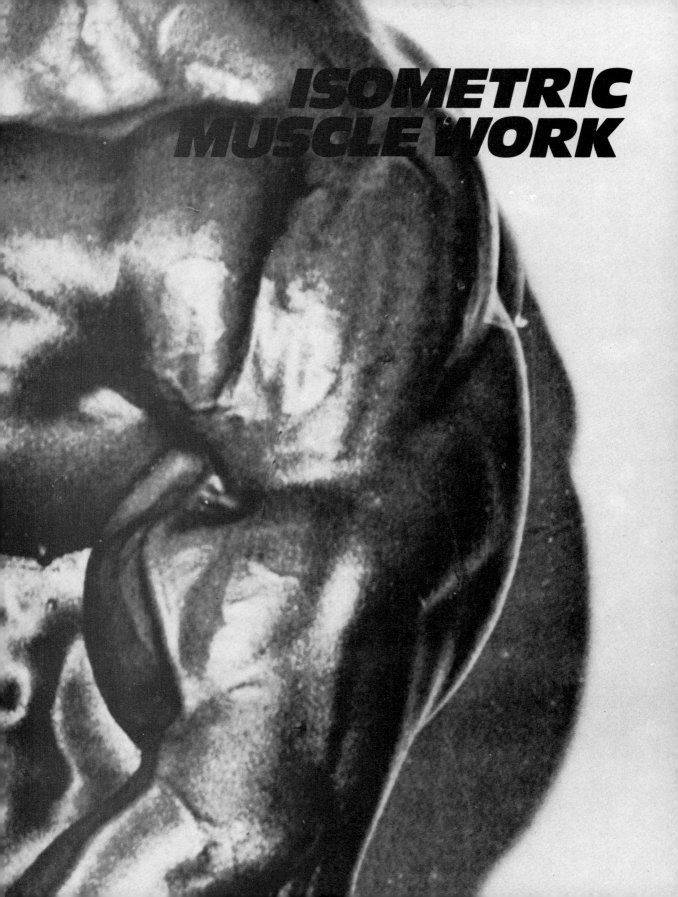

ISOMETRIC MUSCLE WORK

Isometric muscle work

There are two main types of grip training: one is known as isotonic exercise, and the other is isometric exercise. Isotonic exercises are those in which the muscles work through a wide range, alternately contracting and relaxing. Most of the standard exercises come into this category.

The other group, isometric exercises, is where the muscles work statically, at a fixed length, as in holding a position or straining against an immovable object. In isometric contraction all the muscle energy is used in tension and none in movement, for the muscles thus used remain the same length throughout the exercise.

In sport, the gripping muscles are often used statically, as in holding rackets, clubs and bats, or in throwing implements, so a few words on functional isometric work would be appropriate.

Although the isometric principle has been known since 1928 it was not until the early 1950s that Muller's research in Germany indicated that startling gains in strength could be obtained by isometric contraction. Less than ten years later, weightlifters associated with Bob Hoffman in York, Pennsylvania, greatly popularised isometric exercises and started a nationwide craze in the USA. Hoffman sold many isometric devices and wrote numerous articles and books on the subject, but unfortunately this introduction of isometrics coincided with the York lifters earlier experiments with anabolic steroids so there was considerable debate on whether drugs or isometrics produced the sensational results.

Apart from the specificity of grip strength, the greatest advantage of isometrics is that muscles can be worked strongly in a minimum amount of time and with few after-effects in terms of tiredness or aching muscles. Indeed, in less than a total of two minutes working time, a variety of exercises can be completed. Each strenuous contraction is performed for 5 to 10 seconds. It is important that you continue to breathe freely – there is a great tendency to hold the breath, and this should be avoided. The simplest and most specific isometrics are with the objects used in your sport, racket or golf club or whatever. You take your usual grip but squeeze with all your might, as hard as you possibly can, and hold this for five seconds. Even if your sport entails using one hand only, grip with each hand in turn as this will help to maintain balance and get even better results. Each week you should add a second to the contraction time, and at the end of a couple of months your grip will be greatly improved. These exercises can be done daily, but no more than twice per day, at least six hours apart.

There is another aspect of isometric work which should be explained so that it can be applied for various requirements. Sometimes it is necessary for a strong, secure grip to be sustained for a period of time with the body in different positions, such as when a powerlifter does a maximum dead lift, which would take several seconds to perform. To train isometrically for this, the lifter should use not one but **three** contractions: the first with the bar at its lower level, the second

Tim Belknap (Mr World) pays plenty of attention to his forearms

with the bar in the mid position, say at knee height, and finally with the body upright or almost upright. He could do this with the bar loaded to above maximum and then placed on blocks or stands at the various levels; or he could use one of the special power racks with holes at different heights in which the bar is placed, or braced against pegs in the holes. The 5- to 10-second contractions are still used, but because there are three contractions most trainers prefer

not to go above eight seconds.

Many of the exercises described elsewhere in this book are isometric exercises for the grip, although other muscles may be used isotonically; pinch gripping and the rectangular fix are typical examples. If the sport or activity in which you are interested demands grip strength of an endurance nature, then an alternative approach to the development of grip endurance is to do exercises such as the dead lift, pinch grip or chinning the bar

in the usual fashion, doing the stipulated number of repetitions, but after the target number of reps have been completed the last repetition should be held as long as possible, until the grip gives out.

While many people have seen isometrics as one of the passing fads in fitness training, there is a definite place for this mode of training in developing grip strength if applied correctly as described in this section.

The isometric exercises shown here employ a piece of chain and a pair of expander handles.

The model is Alexander Zass who, when captured during war-time, escaped so often that eventually his captors restrained him with shackles and chains. He devised a series of isometric exercises using these bonds and grew in strength in spite of his confinement.

The device is pulled in the positions shown, holding the contractions in each position for five seconds.

As you progress, greater effort should be used in these static pulls. Eventually you should be doing each exercise three times; the first set with about 50% effort to warm up, the second set with around 75% effort and the final set worth maximum effort. It is particularly important to avoid holding the breath in the final set.

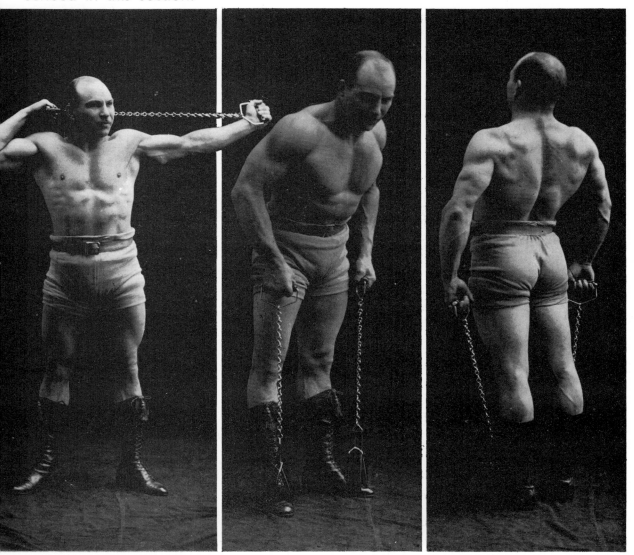

Bending nails

A standard test of strength, and one that will give your whole hand and wrist and forearm a terrific workout, is the feat of bending 6-inch nails. These standard nails are obtainable from any ironmonger or do-it-yourself shop. Also needed are two small pads of cloth or leather to aid in gripping the nails, and to prevent injury. Sticking the pointed end or even the head into your palm can be very painful and dangerous. Many performers go so far as to file off the points of the nails, thus avoiding the risk of puncturing the hand.

Bending nails and spikes is a splendid way to display your strength. However, this form of strength exhibition requires some knowledge as to how it should be done. You have to discover the best position in which to apply your strength before you commence.

Naturally, nails vary in size and bending resistance, and it is sensible to try to obtain some of the softer varieties of nails as your introduction to this test of strength!

One of the easiest ways of bending nails or iron bars is across the thigh. Always remember carefully to wrap the ends of the nails or jagged bars, before attempting to bend them. Grip each end of the nail firmly, and, with the thigh outstretched slightly, place the nail across the thigh; exerting pressure, bend the nail or bar as close together as you can, finishing the closure by placing the nail in cupped hands between the thighs – with combined thigh and hand strength, close the nail or bar until the ends touch, or nearly so.

Arnold Schwarzenegger. Note development of forearms

The next method is to grip the short bar or nail with an undergrip, with the little fingers of each hand touching. You now exert pressure in an upwards direction, at the same time applying an inwards and downwards pressure with the little-finger area of the hand. Ensure that once you feel the nail bending you continue to exert your strength until the nail is completely bent.

If at first you do not succeed in your nail-bending attempts, simply continue daily to attempt to bend the nails; by these efforts alone you **will** soon develop the strength to complete the feat. **The strength to bend the nails will surely come with renewed practice.**

In all nail-bending positions, to finish bending the nails to make the ends meet (or nearly so!) place the nail between both palms and squeeze it shut by interlocking your fingers.

The most popular method of bending nails or bars is the following. Commence with the nail safely wrapped and held firmly with palms facing downwards, in other words using an overgrip with the thumbs and index fingers together. Holding the nail at chest height, firmly bend downwards on the outside edge of the nail, and upwards at the centre of the nail. To complete the bend, as in the other methods, finish off by interlocking the fingers and crushing the nail with chest and arm power. Another way to close the nail after bending it as far as you can go with the preliminary method, is to place the nail on its side on a firm surface and then try smashing it closed with the side of the fist, using a karate-type blow. Speed is important in nail-bending and breaking; the faster you bend and straighten the nail or bar the easier it becomes.

Arnold Dyson of England, Mr Universe in 1953 and winner of the world bar and nail-breaking championship in 1957, weighed in his best condition 215 lb at a height of 6 feet, with a 51-inch chest. Dyson, a top bodybuilder and at one time a pro wrestler, was a great champion at bending nails. Consider the following account:

Dyson bent and **broke** a $^7/_{16}$ x 12-inch best-quality iron bar in the incredible time of only 25 seconds. He also broke four 6-inch 3-gauge nails in 59 seconds, both times being official, with even quicker times achieved in training.

Prior to winning the nail championship, Arnold had beaten the late Geoff Morris of Southport who was himself a superb all-rounder, excelling in bending nails and bars. Arnold Dyson on that occasion broke five nails, each 6 inches long, in just 1 minute 35 seconds, to win the British bar and nail-breaking championship (March 1954).

Other records of Arnold's are:
1. Breaking one 3-gauge 6-inch nail in 5 seconds.
2. Breaking one 4-gauge 6-inch nail in 10 seconds.
3. Breaking six 4-gauge 6-inch nails in 60 seconds.

Dyson wisely suggests that when training to break or bend 6-inch nails or bars, you should soak your hands in surgical spirit to harden them. He also advises you to wrap the nails or bars in canvas or a similar covering to protect your hands, and to safeguard yourself against injuries. Arnold relates how he once sustained a deep four-inch-long wound, when a bar he was attempting to bend broke suddenly, sticking into his arm. So take heed and be prepared. You will also find when attempting to break nails or bars that the metal becomes very hot and can burn you. A canvas covering guards against this.

John Massis, better known as World Champion teeth lifter, shows his strength bending an iron bar

Bar bending

The annually televised world's strongest man contest is surely a severe test of strength, taxing to the limit the strongman finalists from many countries. The programme consists of a variety of events designed to test the competitors' all-round strength. From year to year, occasional changes are made in the programme, with some strength feats or stunts proving impracticable or perhaps too dangerous. One event which has often been included, providing a constant and universally accepted standard of power, is the bar-bending contest. The contestants usually commence with hot-rolled-steel bars 3 feet long and half an inch in diameter. Gradually the competitors are eliminated as thicker bars are used. The event calls for the bars to be bent double, so that the ends come within 8 inches of each other; the bars are to be bent either over or around the neck, or by the more popular method of pulling down on the bar, which is supported on the towel-protected head. In other events the bars are longer but also thicker, with diameters of up to an inch.

Charles Atlas, whose real name was Angelo Siciliano, surely the most well-known and popular of all the originators of home training courses, first started his career by demonstrating chest expanders on Coney Island. Atlas was indeed exceptionally strong, having done much all-round strength training including lifting weights, along with his sports and athletic abilities. (He was a good American football player.) Atlas' famous "free book" explaining his renowned **dynamic tension** course shows photos of him pulling cars and railroad trucks, and also bending a 5-foot-long one-inch-thick iron bar. Atlas was well above average strongman standard at grip feats, and kept a grip on life until his 80s. Even at 77 years of age, his physique was excellent enough to be featured in his own adverts. He certainly deserves credit for starting more men on the road to physical excellence than perhaps any other.

Of course, strength is not a male prerogative! There were, and are, many fine strongwomen, most of whom excel at bending bars and similar stunts. One who springs to mind immediately is Joan Rhodes, a popular and vivacious strongwoman who was at the height of her fame in the late 1950s and early 1960s. Joan once competed in figure contests, but realising her greater strength she eventually concentrated on a strongwoman act, becoming the top artiste in that sphere. She began her strength act as a busker outside Charing Cross Station bending 6-inch nails. Her popularity zoomed, and she ended keeping company with all the top stars of the day, appearing at top theatres and on radio and television worldwide. Joan Rhodes has also been featured in many magazines. Joan could bend a $5/8$-inch steel bar into a horseshoe shape, and she bent longer bars up to $1\frac{1}{2}$ inches wide while holding the bar at the centre with her teeth. She also easily bent and broke 6-inch nails, and found tearing massive telephone directories in half child's play. I believe she is still doing so.

Overleaf: **Joan Rhodes**

Developing grip strength

Single finger lifts

The lifting of heavy weights with a single finger has long been a favourite exhibition of strength by professional strongmen. Some incredible weights have been lifted, and I include here some examples of various famous strongmen and their achievements to give you an idea of the possibilities of single finger lifting. To lift the heaviest of weights, you require a special **finger ring**, which is made of a short length of quarter-inch mild steel, placed in a vice and hammered into shape around a length of pipe to make a hole for your finger. The hole into which your finger goes is padded, usually with lengths of tape, just allowing room enough for your finger to fit into the hole. On the other end of the ring you bend the pipe or length of steel into a hook, from which you can hang the weights. You must of course use strong enough steel which will not bend out of shape when a heavy weight is hung from it. As with all other forms of strength, you simply work your way up, using heavier and heavier weights as your strength and confidence grows.

Some examples of finger lifting . . .

The great Eugen Sandow, who was the supreme showman, always tried to introduce some novelties in his various stage acts. He would lift a barbell with enormous spherical weights overhead, bearing the weight on one hand. Upon returning them to the floor, the bells on each end would open and a man would then step out of each bell! In the same act Sandow lifted a stooge whose stage name was Goliath with one finger. Goliath weighed 27 stone, being 6 feet 3 inches tall, with huge hands and feet.

Louis Cyr, the famous French Canadian old-time strongman, lifted 552½ lb with his middle finger in Chicago on 7 May 1896.

Philip Brumbach, who was the father of the famous strongwoman Katie Sandwina, lifted 441 lb with his little finger, and 642 lb with his middle finger.

The old-time magazine called *The Police Gazette*, more affectionately known as "The Pink 'Un" because of its page tint, mentioned some incredible finger lifting feats by Warren Lincoln Travis (1876-1941). Travis, who concentrated mainly on hip and thigh lifts, also specialised in finger strength. He lifted 1,105 lb with just two fingers – one on each hand – and on 5 November 1907 he lifted with one finger the huge weight of 667 lb, this being approximately equivalent to lifting four grown adults with one finger.

Jack Walsh, born 28 February 1930, height 5 feet 9 inches, bodyweight 185 lb, beat Travis's record with 670 lb on 13 November 1950, and later upped that figure to 732 lb. Perhaps he has done even more by now, as he is an incredible man. For example, he has done a back lift of 4,638 lb and lifted 1,000 lb with just two fingers (one on each hand).

Regarding finger lifting Jack Walsh says: "I think I should explain here that you use a ring on your finger to do the one-finger lift, and you must be able to stand great pain when doing it. This isn't a lift you practise, you just do it and lift more and more weight as you gain strength. Your finger takes a beating and can get mighty sore if you try to do reps in this lift. After a limit lift, my finger is

swollen and sometimes black and blue. It takes weeks to get so I can use it again.''

So take heed of an expert's warning.

So far as I am aware the heaviest weight of all for this single finger lift was reported in *Strength and Health* magazine in 1941 by weightlifter S. Weeks, who claimed to have lifted 760 lb with his middle finger using a tightly padded finger ring.

Above: **Warren Lincoln Travis, an old-time strong man who could lift 667 lb with one finger**
Right: **Pioneer muscle star Eugen Sandow with Goliath. Sandow used to lift Goliath with one finger**

These lifts are all exceptional, taking almost unbelievable strength and the ability to withstand pain. You can easily tear ligaments and pull muscles, as well as damaging body tissue, carrying out such stunts. So take great care if you try them.

Strength stunts using wall bricks

The common wall brick can be used in various ways as an exercise and as an easily available test of strength. Regular tradesmen in the building industry, such as masons, bricklayers and building labourers, usually develop well above average grip and forearm strength with their continual handling of bricks. I personally had much experience of this in my youth, often unloading tens of thousands of bricks daily at a time when the normal lorry-load of London wall bricks was 6,500. We used cut-out "gloves" made from old motor-car inner tubes to try to protect the hands from cuts and abrasions when throwing,

catching and stacking bricks. All this was a good hand toughener. Modern progress has now eliminated much of this hard labour.

The world record (at the time of writing) for laying standard wall bricks is held by Jo Raglan from Illinois, who is credited with laying nearly 58 bricks a minute. Aided by an assistant, Raglan laid 3,472 bricks in just one hour. More recently (October 1979) Ralph Charnock, from Benfleet, Essex, laid 698 bricks unaided in one hour. The bricks were laid correctly according to the

Below: **World Record brick lift by Garry Windebank**

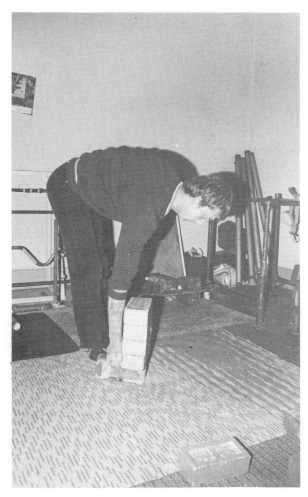 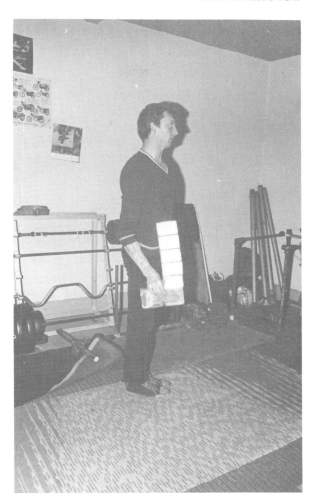

Above: **Mike Bolton showing the start and finish of a difficult brick lift. Each brick weighs an average of 8 lb**

recognised standards of the Guild of Bricklayers.

For sheer endurance it is hard to beat the long-distance brick-carrying record of Ron Hamilton, who carried in his ungloved hand a brick, hanging downwards, for 40 miles. I don't suggest that you try to emulate this feat.

Geoff Capes, several times winner of the title of Britain's strongest man, has thrown a wall brick over 146 feet, which is an enormous distance to fling such an object.

Many karate experts practise their skill on slates, planks and wall bricks. An example of really tough hands is Billy Corbett, a karate expert from Washington, who on 29 April 1972 broke a pile of 5,000 (yes, five thousand) bricks in half with his bare-hand karate chop. He took 17 hours to complete this amazing record, sometimes breaking as many as eight bricks at a time. To develop such toughness of the hands, karate devotees normally start off by hitting the normal boxing punch bag, then advance to striking padded planks, then unpadded softwood planks, and finally graduate to hardwoods and masonry. To toughen fingers, they usually fill a bucket with sand and then punch into it with the fists or open hand. Remember, however, that karate is a specialist skill and should be learned only under expert instruction.

Returning to our subject of wall bricks and lifts, see the illustrations for some other ideas of lifts and stunts for you to attempt.

To conclude this short section, I will mention Hermann Goerner's feat of lifting to chest height fourteen wall bricks weighing 123½ lb (56 kg) with his two hands pressing laterally inwards. This is a stunt frequently practised by anyone in contact with bricks in the building trade. Naturally bricks vary in size, texture and weight. Some have "frogs", the indented part meant to act as a key when filled with mortar; some are smooth-faced and harder to lift. Normal-faced bricks become hard to lift in such a fashion once you try it with eight or more bricks — there is a tendency for the group to collapse in the middle unless gripped very tightly with the hands. This requires enormous chest and upper back strength.

It's useful to know that if at present you have no apparatus or training equipment, you can always experiment with lifting the various types of wall bricks, including concrete blocks, breeze blocks and cinder blocks.

Just a warning . . .

The feats of strength quoted are not necessarily the ultimate: records are constantly improving. So do not bet your last dollar on my figures — they may have since been beaten!

Gary Windebank's World Record 2½ tonnes of bricks pushed 331 feet 11 inches

Wrist Wrestling

One of the most popular activities associated with forearm and grip strength is wrist wrestling, a bar-room sport which has developed into a championship event in America. The competitor places his elbow on the table, bar top or similar support, and endeavours to press his opponent's hand down onto the table.

Mean practitioners of the art will sometimes grip tight and dig their fingers into their rival's hands; and a common but acceptable strategy is for a competitor to flex his wrist and turn it to extend the wrist of his opponent, who is thus put at a disadvantage. Practice of this sport will undoubtedly build grip strength, and a fine exercise for those wishing to excel in this activity is illustrated by Bert Elliott, who is pulling against a rubber belt substituted for the resistance provided by an opponent. This allows repetitions to be performed and permits progressive loading. Rubber straps, bicycle inner tubes and chest expander springs can all supply the resistance required.

Opposite: **Scottish Wrist Wrestling Championship final, won by Billy Dunlop of Ayr (right)**

Below: **Bert Elliott—arm wrestling exercise**

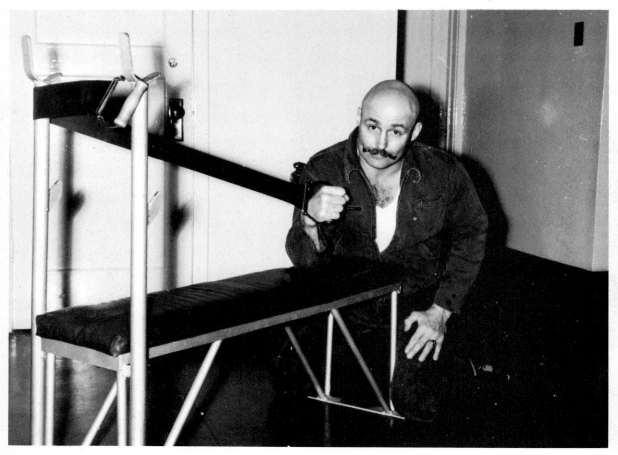

Miscellaneous feats of gripping strength

Salvius, a strong man from ancient Rome, was reputed to be able to climb a ladder with weights of 200 lb tied to both his hands and another 200 lb tied to his feet. This would have required enormous strength of grip.

Richard Joy from Kent, a strong man of the Middle Ages, was said to break with his bare hands a rope which had a breaking strain of over 35 cwt.

Czar Peter the Great of Russia was a huge man, some 6 feet 8 inches in height, with great strength, being able to bend and break silver coins in his hands.

Maurice Saxe of Fontenoy could break horseshoes with his bare hands.

Thomas Topham (1710-1749), a famous early English strongman, was a publican living in London. He was not a huge man compared to some, being about 5 feet 10 inches tall and around 14 stone in bodyweight, but he possessed enormous all-round strength. He excelled in gripping feats, many of which are faithfully documented in a contemporary author's witness of his strength, namely Dr John Theo Desagulier's book entitled *A Course of Experimental Philosophy* (London, 1763). Topham could snap pipe stems in his outstretched fingers, and could crush pipe bowls by squashing them with his first and second fingers with lateral pressure. He is credited with being able to lift 244 lb overhead "easily" with just his little finger. He bent thick pokers by striking them on his forearm, and easily bent thick iron bars around his neck. He could crush pewter drinking pots with his grip, bend iron pokers in his hands, and roll up pewter plates with his fingers. No wonder his diminutive wife was always angry! Topham's marriage was a disaster, and he committed suicide at an early age.

Maxick, whose real name was Max Sick — he changed it for obvious reasons — was without doubt the world's greatest exponent of the art of muscle control. Maxick used to thump the top of champagne bottles so hard with his hand, that the bottom of the bottle would fly off — not a stunt I recommend you to try, as it would be dangerous. Even more hazardous was the feat of Charles Vansittart ("the man with the iron grip"), who could crack champagne bottles in the crook of his arm by tensing his biceps muscle. Try cracking walnuts this way; it is nearly as hard, and not as dangerous.

Throughout the history of strength, only a handful of men have been capable of bending or breaking coins by the pure strength and power of their fingers. Best known of all for this ability was the Polish strongman Franz Bienkowski, whose stage name was "Cyclops". Known as "the coin breaker", Cyclops broke coins in front of many reputable witnesses, using just thumbs and fingers. Similarly famed for his fabulous grip was Charles Vansittart, who could bend and break an English old penny by holding it in one hand with finger and thumb pressing it against the ball of his other thumb, continually bending it until it broke. The old English penny was quite a large coin; a modern decimal penny is smaller and therefore harder to grip, and so is almost impossible to bend.

Another British strongman credited with coin bending was William P. Caswell, who also broke pennies.

Please do not try *to copy any of these dangerous stunts, they are included for interest, not for you to try to emulate.*

John Marx (or Grunn) was a professional strongman from Luxembourg (1868-1912) who became famous for his ability to break genuine horseshoes. Marx, who called himself "The Luxembourg Hercules", excelled in forearm strength. On one occasion at an exhibition in Paris in 1905 he broke three horseshoes in succession in just 2 minutes 15 seconds. Apparently he had larger hands than average, and he regularly practised lifting thick-handled

dumb-bells, an occupation at which very few others could beat him.

Card tearing is recognised as a fine feat of strength, with some great records being established. Al Treloar, an early physique man who could probably be called the first physique winner of the Mr America type, used regularly to tear in half four packs of playing cards.

Another old-time professional strongman was Paul Von Boeckmann, a physical-culture instructor and also, as was the vogue in the early 1900s, a conductor of a "muscle by mail" business. Boeckmann, who must have trained as many as a quarter of a million pupils, certainly practised what he preached. His power ranged from that of endurance, e.g. cycling over 1,500 miles in 15 days, to weight-lifting records. In the realm of grip strength, he devoted much practice to tearing cards, and could tear a normal pack of cards

Reg Park raises a London taxi-cab

Six men in a diesel-engined car passing over the forearm of Joe Falzon of Malta

into *eighths*. Even more amazingly, he used to tear out a full piece of the pack, about the size of a 10 pence piece. Even at the age of 68, he could tear a semi-circular piece from the spine or bound end of the huge New York telephone directory. He could also do three push-ups using one finger only.

Arthur Saxon lifted overhead a weight of 298 lb (135 kg) hooked into his little finger.

G. W. Rolandow (1874-1940), a Swiss strongman whose real name was Wuthruck, became a naturalised American and was one of the best of that era's strongmen, having remarkable all-round prowess both as an athlete and as a strength performer. He was best known for his outstanding ability at jumping; for example, he would jump forwards and backwards over a 200-lb barbell held in his hands as if jumping over a broomhandle, and he could jump over a

3-ft high by 2-ft wide table while holding in each hand a 75 lb dumb-bell. In our specialised subject of grip strength, Rolandow's feat of tearing in half three packs of cards plus an extra six cards together at one time, demonstrated his great power.

Old-timer John Y. Smith from Boston, a remarkable American strongman only about 5 feet 6 inches in height and never weighing more than 165 lb, once carried a 220-lb barbell in his right hand and a 200-lb barbell in his left hand, and then walked with both barbells for over 75 yards. As each barbell also had very thick handles, this was an exceptional feat of gripping power and indeed all-round body strength.

Arthur Dandurand, a Canadian from Montreal, was a strongman who had very powerful forearms developed by pushing loaded wheelbarrows in training. He once wheeled a load of lead ingots weighing 4,300 lb for a distance of 23 feet. Arthur's most famous feat of strength was lifting unaided to his shoulder a Ford motor engine weighing 455 lb. After lifting it to his shoulder, he then walked a distance of 84 feet before lowering it to a bench. When over the age of 40 Arthur could still do a single-handed dead lift of 552 lb. Dandurand was one of Canada's greatest of all strongmen, following in a great line of tradition.

The celebrated French Canadian strongman Louis Cyr (5 feet 7 inches tall, weighing about 300 lb) was in his time a rightful claimant to the title of strongest man in the world. Cyr had huge and powerful forearms, and he was un-beaten in his day at lifting cumbersome rocks, logs and barrels. As was the common practice then, he lifted dumb-bells with thick handles, including one weighing 525 lb single-handed. Louis Cyr had very strong hands and fingers, and once lifted 552½ lb with just one finger.

Eugen Sandow, the most famous of all old-time strongmen, although nowhere near the strongest, also had powerful fingers, being able to "chin" the bar with any one of his fingers or thumbs, hook-ing finger or thumb through a strong rope. Sandow first made a name for himself at the start of his career by going around the towns where he intended to perform his strength act and breaking the then popular "try your strength" hand grip machines.

Another pioneer strongman, the diminutive yet magnificent former physical-culture instructor Adrian Schmidt, could "chin" himself for ten repetitions, using just his right middle finger.

Although chinning the bar effectively develops grip power, an even better exercise for the hands is rope climbing. If you want a target to aim for, consider Don Perry's feat. In 1954 Perry, from Illinois, climbed a 20-foot rope in just 2.8 seconds. An early silent movie Tarzan, actor and gymnast Frank Merrill, climbed a 45-foot rope from a **seated** start, i.e. without jumping from the standing position, in just 16 seconds.

More tough guys . . .

Peter B. Cortese from the USA achieved a one-armed dead lift of more than three times his bodyweight. He lifted 370 lb (167 kg), and weighed only 116 lb.

One of the toughest men of all time in the realm of grip strength was Mac Batchelor of Los Angeles, undefeated champion at wrist wrestling for over a quarter of a century, from 1931 to 1956.

Mac, a Scotsman who emigrated to the States, later became one of Amer-ica's finest strength athletes, specialising in feats of grip strength. He became even more famous for his prowess as a wrist wrestler, taking on all comers, usually in saloons or bars, often tackling as many as a dozen opponents daily without losing. Mac was an authority on strength, and wrote many fine articles on the subject in the top muscle magazines. A large man, 6 feet 1 inch tall, with a bodyweight of around 300 lb, chest 52 in, arms 19 in, he demonstrated his finger strength by crushing metal bottle caps between them. Once he crushed over five hundred in twenty minutes. Mac could pinch grip two 80-lb (38-kg) discs between fingers and thumb, and carry them over thirty feet. He could also hang single-handed from a rope, despite weighing about 300 lb. Some of his other feats of strength were: climbing a 20-foot ladder with a 600-lb horse strapped to his back; walking 342 feet with a 600-lb telephone pole on his shoulder; doing barbell curls with over 200 lb and dumb-bell curls with 90-lb

dumb-bells; and doing three sets of twenty repetitions in the hip lift with 3,000 lb. A real tough guy!

Hermann Goerner (1891-1956) was for my money the greatest strongman of all time, weight for weight, and had the best all-round ability.

His life story and accounts of his strength feats are recorded in meticulous detail by Edgar Mueller in his superb book *Goerner the Mighty* (edited by John Valentine and John E. Dawe; published by the Vulcan Publishing Co., 1951).

Goerner was 6 feet 1 inch tall, and usually weighed around 220 to 250 lb, with a neck of nearly 20 inches, chest 50 inches, a 9-inch wrist and 15-inch forearm. When it comes to grip and forearm power, then Goerner was *tops!*

Consider a few examples of Hermann's mighty power . . .

(1) In his early days as an amateur weight-lifter, Goerner ran just over 100 yards in 18 seconds with a 110-lb weight (kettlebell) in each hand. Kettlebells are so named because the ball weight, with the handle on top, resembles a kettle without a spout.

(2) He took about a second to tear two packs of cards (all together) in half, thus indicating he could easily have done more.

(3) At wrist wrestling in Leipzig (now in East Germany) in 1934 he took on six famous international wrestlers, lined them up on one side of a table, and beat every one of them one after the other in about one minute.

(4) He snatched with two hands a 165¼-lb barbell by just pinch gripping

Jack Shanks hoists 462.2 lb with his right hand and 438.5 lb with his left – a total of 900.7 lb, at a body weight of only 174.5 lb. Officially refereed, this was a fine feat of grip strength

the two end discs on 20 October 1931 in Leipzig.

(5) He swung overhead with one hand three kettlebells weighing 166½ lb.

(6) Sitting in a chair he could raise from a table and thence overhead a smooth ball of iron which weighed 220½ lb (100 kg). He did this purely with hand pressure on the sides of the iron ball.

(7) He was famed for his ability at dead lifting, and:

Performed a one-handed dead lift of 734½ lb (333 kg) in Dresden on 20 July 1920.

Did a right-handed dead lift of 727½ lb (330 kg) on 8 October 1920.

Performed an official 663½ lb dead lift on 29 October 1920.

Dead lifted with two hands 794 lb (360 kg), also on 29 October 1920. His body weight was then 220 lb.

Using just two fingers of each hand, dead lifted a barbell weighing 595¾ lb on 30 November 1933.

With one hand dead lifted 734½ lb in Dresden on 20 July 1920 (the weight was a square block of sandstone with an attached handle).

Lifted a 441-lb barbell, plus two men, one standing on each end of the bar, the total weight being 830 lb.

Many other feats are described in Edgar Mueller's book, and I strongly recommend lovers of strength lore to attempt to find a copy of this now out-of-print volume.

Alexander Zass, "the amazing Samson", who topped the bill in theatres and circuses wherever he travelled, specialised in the bending of iron bars and the breaking of chains, an ability which he developed while a prisoner of war in World War I. Zass devised a unique series of exercises while in prison to

maintain and improve his strength. The exercises were basically isometric in type. He practised religiously, attempting to bend or break the bars or chains which held him captive. Eventually, he could snap strong chains and bend three iron bars into decorative scrolls. In 1925 he bent an iron bar 9 inches long and half an inch thick into a U-shape. Alexander Zass died in Essex in 1962, remaining very strong even in his seventies.

Another great bender of iron bars was J.C. Tolson, a Yorkshireman, who exhibited as a professional strongman under the title of the mighty Apollon. At a height of 5 feet 6 inches, and weight of around 165 lb, he demonstrated fine grip strength, bending iron bars, tearing packs of cards into quarters, breaking chains, lifting heavy weights overhead with one finger, and bending together at one time four 6-inch nails. For many years Tolson ran a mail-order muscle course, called "The Apollon" course, in which the pupils were taught how to bend and break nails, as well as how to develop all-round body strength. The course was based on the normal body exercises of press-ups, squats etc., plus the use of a variety of short bars at which the pupil could extend his energies, eventually being able to bend most of them. This was in fact an early type of isometric strength system, much the same as Zass's. The continual practice of this type of exercise eventually produced the real strength and ability to succeed at bending bars and nails.

Another Apollon was the strength athlete William Bankier (1872-1949), who although only 5 feet 6 inches tall and weighing not much more than 180

lb performed some fine feats of strength, including the carrying of a 24-ft steel rail for over 40 yards. Bankier loved climbing ropes, which is a great developer of the grip. He also regularly trained by pushing heavy wheelbarrows (see Bill Richardson's feat).

Joe Greenstein, the "Mighty Atom", twisted and bent horseshoes in front of many reputable witnesses. He also bent plenty of spikes and bars in his long lifetime, and attended the famous York Fair for over 55 consecutive years to demonstrate his strength. The Mighty Atom's most famous stunt was his genuine ability to bite through nails and metal chains. Never try this, if you value your teeth! He also used to bend coins by holding them between his front teeth and then pushing upwards on the coin with his thumbs.

John C. Grimek could tear 2½ packs of cards into halves. Sig Klein could tear packs of cards into quarters.

Mike Dayton once won his heat in a forearm testing competition stage of the *World's Strongest Man* contest by beating all the other competitors in a wrist-rolling event. He has performed the following stunts to demonstrate his power: Ripped metal licence plates in half, bent in half a heavy metal file, bent 1-inch thick iron bars, bent a rifle barrel in half, and using his karate skills he has smashed through concrete blocks. Now rapidly becoming the greatest exponent of strength feats in modern times, Mike has specialised in certain stunts that remain uniquely his – the ability to break regulation handcuffs, and his dangerous act of dropping into a hangman's rope without injury. Both these are highly dangerous. Do **not** try to copy them, especially the one with the rope, as several former strongmen have seriously

Alexander Zass—early isometric exercises

hurt or killed themselves in similar attempts.

Bill Richardson featured in the *Guin-*

Left: **Mike Dayton, karate expert, smashing concrete blocks**

Below: **Bill Richardson, 'The Black Hulk', using a preacher bench**

ness Book of Records for pushing a loaded wheelbarrow of wall bricks weighing over 3,700 lb. Bill was Mr. Europe and NABBA Amateur Mr Universe 1980; he is now a professional calling himself ''The Black Hulk''. Bill excelled in the sport of wrist wrestling, remaining unbeaten as far as I know.

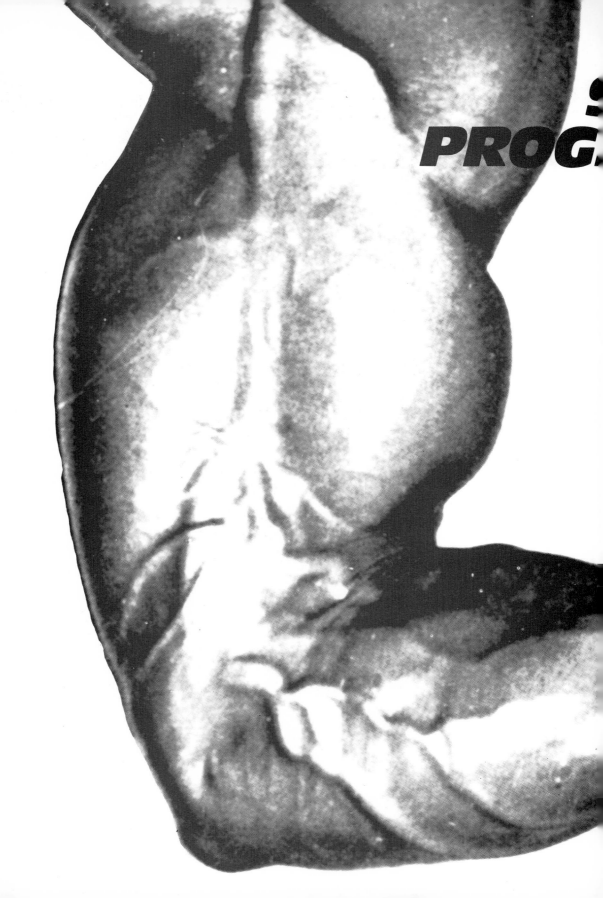

PROG

ECIALISED EXERCISE
AMMES FOR SPORTS

Specialised Exercise Programmes for Sports

All sportsmen benefit from regular all-round training sessions in addition to skill training for their particular sport. Basic training routines fit most sports, but naturally there are some areas requiring more emphasis. The following list, although not exhaustive, gives some ideas and suggestions for you to follow to improve your sporting prowess.

Archery

Basic fitness workouts are advised. The flexing of the shaft, holding the bow string with the "tab", both require extra-powerful fingers and forearms. Practise plenty of wrist work using the wrist roller, plus wrist curls with barbell and dumb-bell. For fingers use the standard gripper and practise pulling the bow string with the first three fingers individually.

Athletics

Throwing the discus (2 kg), hammer (7.25 kg) and javelin are all classic events calling for all-round fitness. This is best obtained by practice of the sport itself, and endurance programmes with weights or free exercises using high repetitions of around 15 to 30. Extra hand and grip power is an obvious advantage so practise plenty of lever-bar exercises, hand gripper work, wrist curls with hands both supinated and pronated, and flexibility exercises. Attempt always to work the muscles over their full range.

Basketball

Basketball requires all-round fitness and endurance, with rapid spurts of power in the legs, arms and shoulders, best developed by playing the game plus fitness programmes in out-of-season periods. Lots of high-repetition squats, squat jumps, twisting and turning movements, and dumb-bell work, all aid performance. Powerful hands are a definite asset in this game when throwing and dribbling with the ball. The self-resistance hand exercises in the early sections of this book are of particular value.

Boxing

Modern boxing is a tough, demanding sport calling for practised skills, great endurance and power to punch, block and guard. Early boxers used to toughen up their hands by pickling them in brine. Obviously, fist/wrist and forearm strength are required in punching, and all boxers of note train on full-body workouts plus specialised hand-toughening methods similar to those explained in more detail in the karate section. Road work is a must for staying power in the legs, and running, sprints, bag punching, fast squats, and light workouts with dumb-bells are advisable.

Baseball

This tough, fast and demanding game calls for skill, endurance and strength. Leg exercise is a must for rapid runs, and hand and wrist strength is equally essential for batting and pitching. Weight-training schedules should include lots of squats, low back exercises such as bent-leg dead lifts, rowing, and dumb-bell exercises for the shoulders, including alternate dumb-bell presses and lateral raises. Lever-bar exercises and wrist curls for easier handling of the bat should be incorporated into every workout.

Canoeing

Canoeing needs all-round body power, especially of the legs, back and hands. Obvious exercises with weights include barbell or dumb-bell rowing, which almost simulate the actual rowing event. Lat machines and cable exercises will develop and strengthen the latissimus dorsi, the large muscles of the back which do the work in rowing. Reverse curls for arm power, and exercises such as chins or pull-ups to the bar, will build up strength for canoeing.

Cricket

Cricket definitely demonstrates wrist/forearm ability and power. Using an end-loaded bar, i.e. a lever bar, is a good exercise for this sport, as are dumb-bell wrist curls and flexibility moves using a hand gripper. Also follow an all-round exercise schedule carried out at least twice a week. Catching, and bowling with its inswings and outswings, are both skills requiring finger strength, so the finger exercises described earlier are of particular value.

Cycling

Obviously cyclists need leg power and endurance, with lots of stress being placed on the hands and wrists which have to support much of the upper body. Try high repetition work, half squats to bench, jump squats, and light dumb-bell exercises such as "flying" or lateral raises. Also use hand grippers, and wrist roller work for the fingers. Isometrics too can assist because of the static nature of the upper body in cycling.

Golf

Emphasis is placed on the correct hand grip and swing of the various clubs. The overlapping, interlocking and two-handed grips of the clubs are assisted by developed hand and wrist power. High repetitions of full-range wrist curls, lever-bar exercises, and an all-round fitness routine with weights will improve your game.

Karate

Judo, karate and in fact most martial arts require immense toughness developed over a long period of *randori* or free practice. Endurance and strength can be developed by full-body workouts practised in a fairly brisk fashion to encourage cardiovascular efficiency and muscular endurance. Go through the workout doing one set of each exercise, followed by the next exercise, rather than using the normal set system. Don't rest too long and for progression try going around the whole workout a second or even a third time before adding extra weights. Plenty of abdominal exercise is advised: judo enthusiasts believe that power comes from the abdomen. Do high-rep sit-ups, leg raises, side bends and twists. Hand power is a must for holding on to the costumes normally worn and for maintaining holds against resistance. Gripping devices, dead lifts and roller work are recommended.

Wrestling

It may be a television spectacular with plenty of showmanship thrown in, but it still needs a lot of power — and of course amateur wrestling is as tough a sport as you can find. All-round power is required if this is your chosen sport, and it calls for lots of neck work — shoulder bridging, self-resistance exercises and the use of head harnesses. Lower back strength and all-over body power is best developed with the use of single and two-handed dead lifts, heavy squats and barbell rowing. For wrists and forearms, use wrist curls, wrist rollers, grippers and all-round practice of strength stunts like bar bending and tearing thick books.

Whatever your sport, regular practice of graduated weight training or free exercise schedules, plus frequent practice of three or four of the suggested wrist, hand and grip exercises will be a positive aid to your progress.

It ain't what you do . . .

Warm-up

Regular balanced exercise is an excellent health insurance, making you lose listlessness and sluggishness, and making you healthier and livelier in every way.

There are a number of possible pitfalls on the road to developing a good grip, and among them are over-enthusiasm and over-specialisation. There is a temptation to compile whole schedules of grip exercises, and quite frankly this would be counter-productive, resulting in overwork and imbalance.

For many people two or three selected exercises for daily practice will be sufficient. In such cases care should be taken to vary the nature of the work; for example, one exercise might be the dead lift, in which the gripping muscles work statically; another might be one of the gripping types of apparatus; and a third could be to use a roller weight for the forearms, as these have such a direct effect on hand and wrist strength.

More dedicated trainees, and sports enthusiasts usually come into this category, will wish to do a lot more work, but unless your grip is very much under par it would be advisable to channel your excess energy into schedules catering specifically for your chosen sport. These will, of course, include grip exercises, which should be selected from those described in this book. When grip strength is very important, as it is in many sports, these hand, wrist and forearm movements should be given **priority**. I emphasise this, for in the usual course of events these exercises would normally be placed in the "small muscle group" category, and would take place at the end of a schedule as depletive exercises. But if you place great importance on grip strength I recommend that they should take place immediately after the warming-up period.

Here is a very rapid limbering-up routine which will help you obtain better results and guard against injuries caused by doing strenuous exercises while cold.

Try this rapid warm-up before commencing muscle-building exercises.
(1) Standing upright, with feet spread comfortably apart, stretch upwards at full arms' length, trying to reach the ceiling.
(2) Lower your arms sideways to shoulder level, and make small rapid circling movements to warm up your shoulders.
(3) With arms outstretched sideways, twist from side to side for about twelve repetitions.
(4) Raise on to your toes and perform 10 to 12 deep knee bends.
(5) Regain your breath, and get ready to start your muscle-building exercises.

Principles and Systems

Keep moving between exercises, to keep warm. Train in warm, pleasant conditions. Aim to wear good training clothes, a clean tracksuit and soft flexible footwear. Pay attention to personal cleanliness and hygiene. Train to a **definite** purpose or plan.

There are many, many systems, with an often complicated and bewildering terminology. I will now attempt to list and explain **most** (but not all) of them, although somewhat briefly, to enable the average exerciser to find a path through the muscle jungle.

Each full movement of each exercise is

done for so many repetitions. For convenience this is shortened to reps.

Reps for exercises vary in number according to the results required. Years of experiment have shown that low reps of around 3 to 6 favour increases in **strength**, power lifters always train on low reps. Average reps of 8 to 12 encourage muscle **size**, and high reps of 15 and over are used for the purpose of definition (cuts), weight loss, and **endurance** training.

If you do an exercise for ten reps, it becomes known as one set of ten, written 1 x 10. Beginners are advised to do just one set of each exercise for the first few weeks of training, gradually adding extra sets as their training capability improves.

A weight trainer of 6 months' experience normally uses for most exercises about four sets of ten reps, or 4 x 10.

In the single progressive system the trainee increases the number of repetitions without increasing the weights. The double progressive system, on the other hand, consists of adding repetitions until a given number is reached, after which the weights are increased, returning to the original reps, which in turn are again gradually increased, and so on.

This double system is the basic progression for beginner/intermediate trainers.

are excellent for this type of exercise, weights can be used for the same purpose if you practise high repetitions using exercises which involve large muscle groups.

In this system you normally set the various weights in advance, after which you go from one exercise to the next (with a single set) without resting until you have completed a circuit.

Type training, or anatomic training, was popularised in early British magazines, yet mainly ignored in the USA. Type training resulted from Sheldon's classification of the three basically inherited physique groups, namely ectomorph (the skinny person), mesomorph (the naturally muscular athlete) and endomorph (the fat person).

The basic theory, supported by plenty of evidence, is that fat people should do high reps, with the idea of using up more calories and burning off excess flesh; the naturally muscular type is fortunate enough to gain on any system; and the skinny individual should use just a few basic to medium reps to build strength and muscle size.

Fitness and Conditioning

For fitness and conditioning you have to practise cardiovascular exercise or aerobic exercise. Aerobic simply means "with air", the object being to improve the systems involved in the body's processing of oxygen, i.e. the heart, lungs and blood vessels.

While running, cycling and swimming

No Pain, No Gain

The most common and successful method used in weight training is called the **set system.** In simple terms this means that after performing one set of ten reps you have a brief rest and then commence again with another set. Most trainers of experience use about 4 to 6 sets, finding this sufficient for muscle growth.

Incorporated within the set system is the practice of pyramiding the weights. This means you vary the weights and reps as in the table. Thus you go up and down, like a pyramid.

Set	Weights	Reps
1	light	high
2	medium	medium
3	heavy	low
4	medium	medium
5	light	high

Or you could consider the "push-pull" split routines; one session devoted to the extensors, and one to the flexors.

Muscles continually get into a rut. To gain size even faster, you must from time to time force the poundage and one way to do this is to use forced reps. Basically this means you have to force out those last two or three reps at the end of each set, as it is those which really count for building muscle and strength.

A variation on this theme is assisted reps, in which a training partner helps you, often with just a finger or two, to complete the last couple of repetitions.

Often a partner can assist by giving you vocal encouragement. Scientific experiments have proved what coaches and cheer leaders have always known, that vocal encouragement by coach or team mates or training partners actually increases the strength of athletes, extends their endurance and raises their threshold of fatigue.

Next time you wish to achieve a maximum bench press, for example, get your training partners to encourage you with loud shouts of **"push", "push", "push".** And just watch those weights soar!

When training on a particular isolated muscle, it helps to concentrate your mind on the muscle. This mental aspect of training with a positive approach must not be overlooked. Even the extreme concentration of self-hypnosis is often employed. Hypnotised subjects have been observed to improve on physical performance and strength, the accepted explanation being that hypnosis removes any inhibitions.

Without fear of failure, you can always lift more. This philosophy of overcoming fear is part of Mike Dayton's "chi" system.

A further idea is the **flushing system,** named because of the flushing effect of the blood vessels. An illustration of this, again using the arms as an example, is to perform sets of similar exercises in quick succession. For example, barbell curls, followed by any other form of dumb-bell curl, again followed by barbell curls.

Going to the opposite extreme from circuit training, many trainers get results from the **single exercise plan.** It is obvious that if you direct all of your energies into a single exercise, then on that one movement you will make rapid progress.

High-intensity training: this advanced system, advocated by top star Mike Mentzer and marketed under his name, simply involves the use of maximum weights, using strict style, working to your limit and forcing out the last reps, often needing slight assistance from a training partner who can give finger-tip help to keep the bar moving.

This is very similar to the forced assisted reps system explained earlier. Many people are of the opinion that it is only the last few hard-pushed reps that count, the easier first reps serving just as a "warm-up".

Moderate weight/high intensity means using moderate training weights but concentrating highly on every part of the movement, contracting the muscles fully throughout and at the end of the exercise.

Saturation pumping is the practice of keeping a muscle group continually pumped by training several days in succession with high reps.

What Suits You?

If you discover a system, routine or exercise that really brings results to you personally, then stick to it regardless of what others may say. Do not swap or change routines just for the sake of it. You must, of course, devote plenty of time to basic training before attempting advanced systems.

It is interesting to note that after having had a period when top trainers were advocating (if not practising) multi-sets, now a more common-sense approach has materialised.

The best result-producing routine of all for the majority of trainers is a schedule of eight to ten different exercises, with from six to fifteen repetitions, from three to six sets, and training sessions just three times a week.

Exercise check-list

This is invaluable in compiling schedules, giving a fast and easy reference to the best and most popular forearm exercises.

Bar bending
Bending bottle tops
Book raising with fingers: (1) palm down; (2) palm up
Breaking matches etc between fingers
Brick lifting
Brush lifting

Chair lifting
Chinning (pull-ups) on bar

Finger curls
Finger lifting
Finger pressing
Floor dips on finger-tips

Gooseneck contraction
Gripping devices (mechanical)

Hand clasping
Hand rotating: (1) clockwise; (2) anticlockwise
Holding heavy barbell: (1) at knee height; (2) at waist height; (3) at chest height

Isometric gripping

Leverage bar raising with weight backwards
Leverage bar raising: (1) weight in front; (2) weight behind
Leverage bar wrist circling, with weight: (1) in front; (2) behind

Nail bending

Pinch gripping with flat discs
Preacher wrist curls

Rectangular fix
Rectangular fix with strands (chest
    expanders)
Reverse curl
Rolling up newspapers
Rope climbing

Self-resistance rotation
Self-resistance: (1) for extensors;
    (2) for flexors
Single-handed dead lift
Slow curl
Squashing beer cans
Squeezing a rubber ball
Straddle lift

Tearing papers, books, directories etc
Two-handed dead lift: (1) knuckles
    forward; (2) knuckles backward;
    (3) alternate grasp

Wrist curl with barbell or dumb-bells
    overhanging bench
Wrist curl with barbell, seated:
    (1) palms down; (2) palms up
Wrist curl with barbell, standing:
    (1) barbell behind back; (2) barbell in
    front
Wrist curl with dumb-bells, seated:
    (1) palms down; (2) palms up
Wrist curl with dumb-bells, standing:
    with dumb-bells held at sides
Wrist curl with strands (chest expanders)
Wrist roller: (1) arms extended; palms
    down; winding clockwise
Wrist roller: (2) arms extended; palms
    down; winding anticlockwise
Wrist roller: (3) arms extended; palms
    up; winding clockwise and
    anti-clockwise

Wrist roller: (4) arms bent; elbows in;
    palms down; winding clockwise and
    anticlockwise
Wrist roller: (5) arms bent; elbows in;
    palms up; winding clockwise and
    anticlockwise
Wrist turns with dumb-bells, seated
Wrist wrestling

A Training Plan

Five-month training plan

Month one
Start off with preliminary training using self-resistance exercises without apparatus, which can be practised daily.
(1) Wrist rolls
(2) Self-resistance movements
(3) Press-ups on finger
Continue this for three to four weeks, increasing repetitions and resistance.

Month two
Begin to use light external resistance, wrist rollers, gripping exercises, etc.
(1) Brush lifting
(2) Chair lifting
(3) Gripping device (bell or apparatus)
(4) Wrist roller

Month three
Light weight-training exercises, including wrist curls, wrist roller with heavier weight, etc.
(1) Wrist roller
(2) Wrist curl with dumb-bell
(3) Seated wrist curl with barbell
(4) Rectangular fix

Month four
(1) Dead lift
(2) Reverse curls
(3) Screw curls
(4) Lever bell lifting

Month five
(1) All types of heavy lifting
(2) Nail bending and breaking
(3) Book tearing

Three-month training plan
This detailed training plan gives precise instructions on volume and intensity of training during the initial period, and should serve to guide you in compiling your own workout pogrammes. It cannot be emphasised too strongly that personally-produced training plans, specifically designed to suit your individual needs, will be most effective, provided they are based on the sound principles outlined in this book.

Week	Exercise	Number of sets	Number of reps
1	Hand clasping	2	8
	Press-ups on fingers	2	8
	Gooseneck contractions	2	10
2	Gooseneck contractions	3	10
	Press-ups on fingers	3	12
	Self-resistance rotations	2	8
3	Squeezing rubber ball	2	7
	Tearing books/papers	1	3
	Press-ups on fingers	4	10
4	Squeezing rubber ball	3	10
	Brush lifting	1	8
	Tearing books and papers	1	5

Week	Exercise	Number of sets	Number of reps
5	Squeezing rubber ball	4	10
	Brush lifting	2	10
	Wrist roller, arms extended	2	16
6	Wrist curls, palms down	2	10
	Brush lifting	3	12
	Wrist roller	2	20
7	Dead lift, alternate grip	2	6
	Wrist curls, palms down	2	12
	Wrist roller	2	24
8	Chair lifting	1	6
	Dead lift	2	10
	Wrist curls, palms down	3	10
9	Reverse curls	2	10
	Dead lift	3	10
	Chair lifting	1	8
10	Chair lifting	1	12
	Single-handed dead lift (each hand)	3	8
	Reverse curls	2	12
11	Leverage bell, weight forward	2	10
	Single-handed dead lift	3	10
	Rectangular fix	3	8
12	Single-handed dead lift	3	12
	Rectangular fix	3	10
	Leverage bell, weight forward	3	10

It is important that you do not change the exercise more often than stated. A "butterfly" approach, flitting from one movement to another in every workout, will detract from progress. The sets and reps listed give good progressions, and resistance can be altered to suit individual capabilities. Use loads which make you work hard — this is the way to get speedy results.

Advanced training plan

Here is a very detailed table giving lift-by-lift progressions which will suit the most advanced grip specialists. The principles apply to all such exercises utilising barbells and dumb-bells but the example exercise here is the dead lift, using an alternate grasp and without straps being worn as this would be counter-productive in producing grip strength.

This kind of training is known as pyramid training as it begins with a broad base of repetitions and the weight gradually rises as you peak at the end of the schedule.

Week	Set 1	Set 2	Set 3	Set 4	Set 5	Set 6	Total
1	150 x 10	200 x 5	210 x 4	220 x 3	230 x 2	240 x 1	4700
2	155 x 10	200 x 6	210 x 4	220 x 3	230 x 2	240 x 1	4950
3	160 x10	200 x 6	210 x 5	220 x 3	230 x 2	240 x 1	5210
4	165 x 10	200 x 6	210 x 5	220 x 4	230 x 2	240 x 1	5480
5	170 x 10	210 x 5	220 x 4	230 x 3	240 x 2	240 x1	5040
6	175 x 10	210 x 6	220 x 4	230 x 3	240 x 2	240 x 1	5300
7	180 x 10	210 x 6	220 x 5	230 x 4	240 x 2	240 x 1	5800
8	185 x 10	210 x 6	220 x 5	230 x 4	240 x 2	250 x 1	5860

The total loading is calculated by multiplying the weight by the reps, for example:

Week 1		**Week 8**	
150 x 10	1500	185 x 10	1850
200 x 5	1000	210 x 6	1260
210 x 4	840	220 x 5	1100
220 x 3	660	230 x 4	920
230 x 2	460	240 x 2	480
240 x 1	240	250 x 1	250
	————		————
	4700		5860

Heavy-duty grip strengthening schedule

This extremely advanced workout is intended to produce maximum strength for those involved in high-intensity demands. It is not designed for muscular endurance or muscle size. It should not be continued for long periods, but should be worked into a long-term plan allowing for recuperation between bouts of intensive work.

This could be a follow-up to the work on the dead lift in the previous section. *Increase* every third workout as follows:

Workout

3	240 x 1	250 x 1	260 x 1	270 x 1	280 x 1
6	245 x 1	250 x 1	260 x 1	270 x 1	280 x 1
9	245 x 1	255 x 1	260 x 1	270 x 1	280 x 1
12	245 x 1	255 x 1	265 x 1	270 x 1	280 x 1
15	245 x 1	255 x 1	265 x 1	275 x 1	280 x 1
18	245 x 1	255 x 1	265 x 1	275 x 1	285 x 1

Conclusion

From the great bodybuilding years of the champions John C. Grimek, first NABBA Mr Universe, a great weightlifter and strongman, and Bill Pearl the magnificent multi-title holder, who also demonstrated his power by bending spikes and tearing car number plates in half, to today's Mr Universe and Mr Olympia champions, the common theme is that they **all** paid plenty of attention to developing their forearms to full capacity.

Today's champion physique stars have to be as near to perfection as humanly possible. The days when physique contests were won by the man with the largest chest or biggest biceps are over and gone. Perfect symmetry with maximum all-round muscularity is now required. Current muscle stars pay meticulous attention to all their body parts, including the forearms.

By following the advice and exercises given in this book, you will not only build forearms of impressive size and muscularity, you will also develop truly amazing grip strength.

Good luck!

Bibliography

Grateful acknowledgements are made to the authors and publishers of the following books and magazines, used as references. Readers are advised to obtain copies of any of the following to increase their knowledge of strength and fitness.

Magazines

Bodybuilding Monthly (ed. Dave Williams)
Bodypower and Fitness (ed. Nick Troop)
Health and Strength (ed. Oscar Heidenstam) – Britain's longest-running magazine of physical culture
Iron Man (ed. Peary Radar)
Man's World (out-of-print)
Muscle and Fitness (ed. Joe Weider)
Muscle Magazine International (ed. Bob Kennedy)
Muscle Power (out-of-print)
Muscle Training Illustrated (ed. Dan Lurie)
Muscular Development (ed. John Grimek)
Reg Park magazine (out-of-print)
Strength (out-of-print) – an old magazine, now rare
Strength and Health
Superman (out-of-print)
Your Physique (out-of-print)

Books

Edward Aston, *How to Develop a Powerful Grip*
Leo Gaudreau, *Anvils, Horseshoes and Cannons*
George F. Jowett, *Moulding a Mighty Grip*
George F. Jowett, *Strong Man Stunts Made Easy*
Robert Kennedy, *Beef It* (Sterling, New York, 1983)
Robert Kennedy, *Hardcore Bodybuilding* (Sterling, New York 1982)
Robert Kennedy and Vince Giranda, *Unleashing the Wild Physique* (Sterling, New York, 1984)
Earle Liedermann, *Muscle Building*
Earle Liedermann, *Secrets of Strength*
David Webster, *Barbells and Beefcake*
David Webster, *The Iron Game*
Ben Weider and Robert Kennedy, *Pumping Up: Super Shaping the Feminine Physique* (Sterling, New York, 1985)
David Willoughby, *The Super Athletes*
David Willoughby and George R. Weaver, *The Kings of Arm Strength*
Developing a Powerful Grip and Big Forearms (Strength and Health Publishing Co.)
The Guinness Book of Records (annual)

Photo Credits

The authors and publishers wish to acknowledge with thanks the following for permission to reproduce photographs.

Pete Aitken
Bodypower magazine
Body Power
Mike Dayton
John C. Grimek
Health and Strength magazine
Bob Hoffman

Bill Hunt
Bill Pearl
Power magazine
Pat Sillence
Strength and Health magazine
Joe Weider
Dave Williams

Other photographs are from David Webster's archives and David Gentle's collection.